Eating Your Way to Good Health

Eating Your Way to Good Health

Recipes for Doug Kaufmann's Antifungal Diet

Doug Kaufmann

with Jami Clark, R.N.

MediaTrition Inc.
Rockwall, Texas

Published by MediaTrition
Rockwall, Texas 75087

Second printing

All material herein is for informational purposes only and does not take the place of professional advice from your healthcare provider. Approaches described are not offered as cures, prescriptions or diagnoses. Information is a compiled report of existing data and/or research. The authors and publisher assume no responsibility in the use of this information. Consult your doctor before using any presented information as a form of treatment.

Publisher's-Cataloguing-in-Publication
Provided by Quality Books, Inc.

Kaufmann, Doug A., 1949-
Eating Your Way to Good Health : Recipes for Doug Kaufmann's Antifungal Diet / by Doug A. Kaufmann
p. cm.
Includes bibliographical references and index.
ISBN 0-9703418-5-7

1. Low-carbohydrate diet--Recipes. I. Clark, Jami. II. Title

RM237.73.K38 2003 641.5'638
QBI03-200736

Manufactured in the United States of America

Cover design by Evan Kaufmann.

Eating Your Way to Good Health

If
you always
do what you've
always done....
You'll always get
what you've
always got.

-Doug Kaufmann

Foreword

If you are holding this book in your hands, you've likely read one of Doug Kaufmann's earlier books, seen him on television in shows such as *Know the Cause!,* or perhaps listened to one of his radio shows. You're thinking that his philosophy on health may help you, and you've decided to give it a go. Hang on for the ride of your life, then. Because what you've decided to do — hopefully — is not simply to treat this as yet another diet, but rather to commit yourself to taking on the challenge of beginning a whole new life-style.

Doug has worked for just this kind of decision for more than 30 years. You see, he's made it his lifelong objective to spread the word about how we can safeguard our health against the fungi and fungal toxins that so often contaminate our food supply. Early on, the resistance he met from the medical community convinced him to take his message directly to the public, via newsletters and then through radio and television programs. He has also gone on to publish several books, a website called *knowthecause.com* and a number of newspaper and magazine articles.

Books such as *The Fungus Link 1, 2 and 3,* each covering different symptoms and disease that may be linked to fungus, *The Fungus Link to Weight Loss, The Fungus Link to Diabetes and The Germ That Causes Cancer* contain volumes of data taken directly from medical and biological references. They highlight the role of fungi and their poisonous by-products (mycotoxins) in human disease.

In addition to the above work, Doug travels to cities all over the United States to hold seminars designed to educate the general public as to how to fight fungi and become truly healthy. At each seminar, he takes the time to answer personal questions from the scores of people who line up to meet him one-on-one.

Now, you can benefit from Doug's expertise by using this book to incorporate his philosophy on health into your own life. Remember, getting your body moving and taking nutritional supplements will always be essential. But if you're eating the wrong things, maximum wellness will continue to remain out of your reach, no matter how much you exercise or how many supplements you may take. Follow the correct diet, and you can actually "let food be your medicine."

I wish you hope, strength, joy and persistence in the new life you've chosen for yourself.

-David Holland, MD

Table of Contents

I dipped my toes into the nutrition field in the early 1970's. While working with an ear, nose, and throat allergist in Los Angeles, shortly after coming home from Vietnam, I discovered (thanks to the patients) that many of his patients stopped taking allergy shots because they felt that they were unneeded after merely changing their diets or taking what I considered to be inconsequential supplements. Of course, we initially scoffed at such a ridiculous idea, believing that diet and supplements played little role in respiratory allergy. I vividly recall hearing these stories about diet changes clearing up sneezing, itching eyes, and breathing problems and became adamant that these nice people were just plain wrong! As the saying goes, fool me once shame on you…thereafter, shame on me! I had my medical training to uphold!

If it were one or two patients, I'd chalk it up to coincidence, but each month we'd lose 6-7 patients because they simply stopped eating wheat, corn, or sugar or start taking Vitamin C! Retrospectively, I remember becoming upset as my income depended upon allergy patients getting better on my tiny shots, not on changes they made to their diets. Worse, I began learning that the patients had become proactive with their own health concerns rather than simply relying on me and my shots! Some told me that vitamin C relieved their allergies better than my shots. Others said, when they ate yogurt, their respiratory allergies cleared up within 20 minutes. Another told me that a little sodium bicarbonate in water stopped her acute sneezing attacks.

After the initial disbelief had cleared, I began trying some of this "witchcraft" on my own. Those who know my history also know that, at that time in my life, I was filled with recurrent health problems, to wit physicians would prescribe medications. For a short time, I thought Prednisone was nectar of the gods, so how could a diet void of sugar possibly help me? Without the advances of computers, the Internet or Google, it was difficult to find out that Prednisone was anything else but the perfect drug! The doctor ordered it, it worked, and no one questioned it in the 1970's. Armed only with a library card and a desire to learn, I began trying to understand why this nectar wasn't offered to every sick person in the world! It was really that good!

Side effect information, or the ability for a lay person to locate it, varied in the early years of prescriptive drug use, but thanks to modern technology, today I can tell you that Prednisone is a drug that needs to be avoided, if at all possible. The Internet website www.drugs.com references these side effects of Prednisone;

Prednisone side effects

Get emergency medical help if you have any of these signs of an allergic reaction: hives; difficulty breathing; swelling of your face, lips, tongue, or throat. Call your doctor at once if you have any of these serious side effects:

problems with your vision;
swelling, rapid weight gain, feeling short of breath;
severe depression, unusual thoughts or behavior, seizure (convulsions);
bloody or tarry stools, coughing up blood;
pancreatitis (severe pain in your upper stomach spreading to your back, nausea and vomiting, fast heart rate);
low potassium (confusion, uneven heart rate, extreme thirst, increased urination, leg discomfort, muscle weakness or limp feeling); or

dangerously high blood pressure (severe headache, blurred vision, buzzing in your ears, anxiety, confusion, chest pain, shortness of breath, uneven heartbeats, seizure).

Less serious side effects may include:
sleep problems (insomnia), mood changes;
acne, dry skin, thinning skin, bruising or discoloration;
slow wound healing;
increased sweating;
headache, dizziness, spinning sensation;
nausea, stomach pain, bloating; or
changes in the shape or location of body fat (especially in your arms, legs, face, neck, breasts, and waist).

This is not a complete list of side effects and others may occur. Tell your doctor about any unusual or bothersome side effect.

I was having some of those, but was led to believe that this was just part of my illness "syndrome" that was perpetuating throughout my body. Of course, you caught the sentence that states that "this is not a complete list of side effects and others may occur." My guess is they were concerned about running out of paper and/or the trees used to make the paper that might be needed to make a "complete list" of the side effects of this drug. Granted, some folks may need it and all that I'd ask is that you take advantage of computer search engines to make the decision for yourself. Today many safer approaches are marketed.

With eyebrows now raised, the good Los Angeles doctor and I

began talking about these mysterious healings that his patients were witnessing when they stepped out on their own, leaving our mainstream allergy clinic. Fortunately, this was an honest, caring doctor and we decided to ask other allergy shot recipients if they would begin swallowing supplements and changing their diets to see if these seemingly modest changes would improve their allergic reactions. Many, but not all, noticed varying amounts of relief. This was groundbreaking to us because many of his patients had symptoms, other than those they came to the allergy clinic with, improve! Once they changed, one said that her sleep improved, another that her arthritis improved, while another lost 30 pounds in 14 days on the diet!

Armed with this exciting information, we began to carefully study the "other kind of allergy" that dealt with food instead of airborne pollens, dusts and animal dangers. A controversial food allergy laboratory test was being studied at The Washington University School of Medicine in Saint Louis, MO and within a few months, I caught a flight from LAX to STL to learn more about this test.

We had learned in the allergy clinic that testing people for allergy involved some risk. A few very, very allergic patients experienced what is called "anaphylactic reactions" to the tiny injections, pricks or scratches. Adrenaline was always kept handy because such reactions were life threatening within seconds and adrenaline might have to be used to pull the patient out of the reaction. All the more reason, we thought, to test blood samples for allergies rather than the patients' skin.

The new test had its own set of problems, but it led to newer technology that was, and still is, much needed in all allergists' offices.

These newer generation tests, called enzyme linked immunosorbent assays (ELISA) and RAST (radio allergosorbent test) have improved the field of allergy by standardizing test results while minimizing dangers associated with testing.

Once home from SLT, I began finding that the more we altered our patients' diets, via these new lab test results, the fewer who needed allergy work-ups and shots. When we added certain supplements, the results were even more exciting. Why, then, you may be wondering do we still have so many allergies and so many allergists?

I found allergists to be very nice, very intelligent people, but amazingly protective of their "turf"- skin tests. Although undoubtedly antiquated, most allergists deny that blood tests are anything but high-tech add-ons to their skin tests. And they may be correct…by 1850 standards, perhaps. Allergists live in modern homes with modern plumbing, and drive their modern car to their modern office in modern buildings. Why, then are they comfortable with such outdated diagnostic tools? In 1873, Charles Blackley performed the first allergy skin tests on patients by scratching the surface of their skin, applying pollen to the scratch, and observing the i0nteraction. In 2009, your allergist does the very same tests. If you're going to an allergist hoping for dietary or immune enhancement supplement advice, I'd caution you that such a move is analogous to going to a grocery store to get your engine rebuilt. But I digress!

Laboratory testing and politics aside, scientists are beginning to discover that the foods we eat have chemical components that definitely play a roll in contributing to either good health, or death, depending upon which the patient is seeking. Let's first talk about immune enhancement. Being scientists, these food components must first have names that keep the lay public from understanding them. Lycopene in tomatoes, sulphorane in broccoli, falcarinol in carrots, for example, should be called "tomatopene," "broccophan," and "falcarrotinal!" That way, we'd know what foods the components were found in. Without expounding upon the nature and human tissues that are positively affected by each component discovered, I can tell you that each has antifungal properties. This is exactly what I expected because I believe that fungus causes many, and perhaps most, symptoms and diseases that we humans suffer from. The fact that so many medical organizations are now listing fresh fruits and vegetables (which is where all of these good component-chemicals are found) as disease prevention foods will one day (I'm hoping) dovetail into the very logical conclusion that the reason these foods are good for you is because they kill fungus and prevent its re-growth. It may take a few more decades before such a conclusion will be drawn, but you don't have to wait for their conclusions! You should be eating fresh broccoli, carrots and tomatoes, and now you know why!

Just a few years ago, scientists unraveled one of the biggest discoveries (I believe) in the past 30 years. As it turns out, about 80% of our immune system lies not in our white blood cells or our lymph nodes, as one might expect, but in our digestive system! Armed with this one piece of information, <u>just imagine how important good food is for good health</u>. But the converse is also true. Bad foods will injure and kill you.

As I stated earlier, "I believe that fungus causes many, and perhaps most, symptoms and diseases that we humans suffer from." You have also learned that fresh fruits and vegetables themselves have potent antifungal properties. But Americans eat far too few fresh fruits and vegetables in favor of what they have been taught was a more sensible and responsible way of eating. Lean meats, whole grains and farm-raised salmon became the "sensible" way of eating. Meat and fat, we were taught, would block veins and cause more deaths than ever before. If only it were really only this simple.

As I changed my diet to accommodate the new government promoted food pyramid in the 1980's, I actually felt horrible! Loading up on 4-6 servings of grains daily just didn't work for me, but my guess is that it was working for cereal companies! In 2002, Dr. Ruth Etzel published in the respected Journal of The American Medical association (JAMA) that our grain supply was "commonly contaminated with mycotoxins" (fungal poisons) and our corn supply was "universally contaminated" with them. Then in March of 2009, a scientist named Martin published this reference to grains in a medical journal called Toxicology and applied pharmacology;

"Our morning cereal may be setting us up for a fungus invasion. This study demonstrates how one mycotoxin (deoxynivalenol-DON) is found in American wheat, barley and corn supply that makes its way to our breakfast tables. Symptoms associated with DON ingestion include diarrhea, vomiting, internal bleeding and ultimately death."

Some years later, I would learn that politics were at play in establishing the food pyramid, which heavily recommended eating grains. It seems that our government digs far deeper than our wallets...all the way into our refrigerators. Author Gary Taubes finally allowed me to better understand why this food pyramid was ever born;

"It was Senator George McGovern's bipartisan, non-legislative Select Committee on Nutrition and Human Needs—and, to be precise, a handful of McGovern's staff members—that almost single-handedly changed nutritional policy in this country and initiated the process of turning the dietary fat hypothesis into dogma." G. Taubes, The Soft Science of Dietary Fat.

One thing is certain; confusion abounds when trying to learn if the Standard American Diet (SAD) nourishes us thereby improving our health, or slowly and methodically kills us. The book you hold in your hands does not promote a fad diet. Since fungus was the first proven cause of disease hundreds of years ago (long before bacteria or virus), I'd say that it finally satisfies Americans' hunger (pun intended) for the truth in diet and nutrition. This diet nourishes people while simultaneously starving parasitic fungus and yeasts. In other words, if you have a fungal infestation, while you eat, it dies.

I will always recommend that you share the information within the covers of this book with a nutritionally competent and knowledgeable doctor. Only he or she knows your medical condition and how diet may affect it. When you're ready to start, make a shopping list and begin knowing all the while that you'll soon be **Eating Your Way to Good Health!**

Breakfast
Dishes

Breakfast Dishes

Mom was right — beginning each day with a nutritious meal really does make a difference in our body and brain power throughout the day. The only difference is, the notion as to what "nutritious" means has changed. Following 25 minutes of morning exercise with a grapefruit and slices of green apple, for example, is a much better choice than cereal, given the fungal metabolites that lurk in our grains. Also, turkey bacon and eggs trump bottled juice and a bagel. Along the same lines, you might try a selection from our salad section for breakfast. At my house, plain yogurt with fresh berries and pecans is a mainstay. Ultimately, in order to achieve optimum health, most of us must embrace a six-letter word — CHANGE!

Breakfast Shrimp

1 pound large shrimp, peeled and de-veined
2 small onions, chopped (about 1¼ cups)
4 tablespoons thinly slice green onion
1 clove garlic, finely minced
4 tablespoons butter
¾ teaspoon salt
½ teaspoon pepper
½ cup water

Heat the butter in a heavy skillet until hot and foaming. Add onion, green onion, garlic, salt and pepper. Stir well, cooking over medium heat for 5 minutes. Add shrimp and cook for 1 minute, stirring often.

Pour in the water and simmer gently for 2 to 3 minutes, or just until the shrimp are cooked through. Season with salt and pepper to taste.

Bacon Avocado Omelet

Smothered in Tomato Sauce

4 large eggs
2 tablespoons water
1 tablespoon butter
3 slices bacon, cooked and crumbled
1 small avocado, peeled and chopped in half-inch cubes
2/3 cup finely chopped seeded tomato
2 tablespoons finely chopped red onion
1 fresh jalapeño chili, or to taste, seeded and minced
2 tablespoons minced fresh cilantro
1 tablespoon fresh lime or lemon juice

Peel and slice avocado into half inch pieces.

In a small bowl, thoroughly combine tomato, onion, jalapeño, cilantro, lime juice and salt and pepper to taste. In a separate bowl, whisk together eggs and water, adding salt and pepper to taste.

In an 8-inch skillet, heat ½ tablespoon of the butter over medium heat until the foam subsides. Pour in half the egg mixture, tilting the skillet to spread it evenly over the bottom. Cook for 1 minute.

Sprinkle half of the omelet with half the bacon and avocado, continuing to cook for one more minute. Fold omelet over the filling and transfer to a plate.

Repeat the above steps to make another omelet, using the remaining ingredients.

Top with salsa and serve.

Asparagus Omelet

½ pound asparagus, trimmed
2 tablespoon butter
1 small clove garlic, minced
4 eggs, lightly beaten
2 tablespoons almond milk
¾ teaspoon minced fresh basil
½ teaspoon salt; 1 dash freshly ground black pepper

Cut asparagus into inch pieces and boil in salted water until tender, about 2 to 4 minutes. Drain thoroughly and set aside. Sauté garlic in 1 tablespoon of butter in an 8-inch skillet and set aside.

In a small bowl, combine eggs, milk, salt, basil and pepper. Recoat skillet with remaining butter. When pan is hot enough (a drop of water sizzles when dropped in), add egg mixture, tipping pan to coat skillet evenly.

Periodically lift up cooked edges, tilt pan and allow uncooked egg to run underneath. When eggs are cooked, but surface is still shiny, place asparagus on one side; slide out of pan, folding remaining side over top.

Breakfast Fruit Salad

3 green apples, diced
2 grapefruits, peeled and chopped
½ teaspoon ground cinnamon
½ tablespoon crushed almonds

Combine ingredients and chill.

One Minute Omelet

2 eggs
2 tablespoons water
1 tablespoon butter, or 1 teaspoon olive oil

Beat together eggs and water until blended. In a 10-inch omelet pan, heat butter until just hot enough to sizzle a drop of water. Pour in egg mixture.

The egg mixture will begin to set immediately at its edges. With an inverted spatula, carefully push cooked edges toward the pan's center, tilting the pan so that any remaining liquid flows onto the cooking surface. Continue to do so until all of the egg is set.

Spoon ½ cup of desired filling into place and fold omelet in half. Invert onto plate and serve immediately.

Bacon Omelet

4 eggs
4 tablespoons almond milk
3 bacon slices, cooked & crumbled (or ham or sausage)
1 tablespoon butter

Whisk together eggs and milk in a bowl. In an 8-inch skillet, heat ½ tablespoon of butter over medium high heat until the foam subsides. Pour in half the egg mixture, tilting the skillet to spread the egg mixture evenly over the bottom, and cook for 1 minute. Sprinkle half the omelet with half the bacon, and cook for one more minute. Fold omelet over the bacon and transfer to a plate. To make another omelet, repeat the above steps using the remaining ingredients. Season with salt and pepper to taste.

Baked Breakfast

6 eggs, beaten
2/3 cup almond milk
1 green onion, sliced
3 slices bacon, cooked and crumbed
1 tablespoon butter
¼ teaspoon salt
1/8 teaspoon pepper

Beat milk and eggs together . Stir in spices, onion and bacon.

Melt butter in a 9-inch frying pan. Pour in egg mixture and bake at 400 degrees for 20 minutes, or until set and golden. Garnish with additional bacon, if desired.

Broccoli Omelet

1 tablespoon olive oil
½ onion, finely chopped
1 cup broccoli, chopped
1 tablespoon minced basil
8 egg whites

In a large frying pan, heat oil over medium heat. Toss in onions and sauté for 5 minutes, or until soft. Add broccoli and herbs and sauté for a few more minutes.

In a small bowl, whisk eggs until foamy. Pour over broccoli in pan and stir a few times to blend, cooking for 3 to 5 minutes. Transfer to oven and bake at 375 degrees for 15 minutes, or until the eggs are set.

Eggplant & Tomato Omelet

8 eggs
1 cup eggplant
4 tablespoons olive oil
1 clove garlic, chopped
½ cup tomato juice
½ teaspoon salt

Peel eggplant and cut into small cubes. Soak cubes in bowl of cold water for ½ hour. Remove, drain and dry well.

Heat 3 tablespoons of olive oil in a skillet. Add eggplant and sauté until it begins to brown. Add tomato juice and then set pan to one side.

Heat remaining olive oil in aother skillet and add eggs. Cook over low heat until set. Spoon eggplant mixture into place and fold egg over to make an omelet.

Country Breakfast

4 large eggs, beaten
2 cups diced ham
½ large green pepper, diced
4 green onions, sliced
3 tablespoons butter
salt and pepper to taste

In a frying pan, melt butter over medium heat and sauté vegetables, ham and seasonings for 3 minutes. Cover and cook over low heat until the peppers are tender, or 2 to 3 minutes. Pour eggs over vegetables, without stirring. Cover and cook until eggs are set, or about 10 minutes. Cut into wedges and serve.

Bacon & Chive Omelet

with sour cream

4 bacon slices, cooked and crumbled
2 tablespoons sour cream
3 large eggs, beaten
1 tablespoon of diced green onions (chives)
1 tablespoon butter
salt and pepper to taste

Mix eggs in a bowl and add bacon, sour cream, and chives. Heat butter in a small skillet until brown. Quickly pour in egg mixture. Stir lightly until set on the bottom. Let stand over heat a few seconds to lightly brown bottom. Fold in half and season with salt and pepper to taste.

Herb Omelet

3 eggs
1 tablespoon butter
1 dash basil
1 dash thyme
1 dash marjoram
1 tablespoon parsley, snipped
1 tablespoon chives, snipped
salt and pepper to taste

Mix eggs in a bowl. Heat butter in a small skillet. Quickly pour in eggs. Stir lightly until set on bottom. Let stand over heat a few seconds to lightly brown bottom. Sprinkle with spices, fold in half and season with salt and pepper to taste.

Scrambled Eggs & Ham

2 ounces ham, cut into strips
4 large eggs, beaten
2 tablespoons green onions, sliced
1 tablespoon butter
¼ teaspoon basil, crushed

In a skillet, combine ham, green onion, butter and basil. Cook uncovered over medium heat for 1 to 2 minutes, or until the mixture is heated through. Beat eggs and pour over ham mixture in skillet. Cook uncovered over medium heat, stirring and turning frequently for 3 to 5 minutes, or until eggs are set.

Shrimp Omelet

2 eggs
¼ cup shrimp, cooked & coarsely chopped (or whole shrimp)
1 tablespoon green onions, sliced
2 teaspoon parsley, chopped
1 tablespoon water
1 tablespoon butter

Beat eggs and water together with a wire whisk and set aside. Heat an 8-inch omelet pan or nonstick skillet over medium heat until hot enough to sizzle a drop of water. Add butter, tilting pan to coat bottom.

Pour egg mixture into pan. As it cooks, gently lift its edges with a spatula, tilting pan so that uncooked liquid flows onto cooking surface. Sprinkle half of omelet with remaining ingredients, fold it in half and transfer to a serving plate.

Scrambled Eggs with Lobster

9 large eggs, beaten
1 eight oz. package cooked lobster
2 tablespoons chives, snipped
½ red bell pepper, stemmed, seeded and minced
5 tablespoons heavy cream
6 tablespoons butter
salt and pepper to taste

In a small skillet, melt 2 tablespoons of butter over medium heat. Toss in bell pepper and sauté 2 minutes. Add lobster and cook a few more minutes, until just warmed through. Stir in chives, cook 30 seconds more and remove from heat.

In a medium-sized, heavy skillet, melt 2 tablespoons butter over low heat. Pour in the eggs and half the cream. Gently scramble with a rubber spatula until mixture thickens, or about 5 minutes. Add remaining cream and 2 tablespoons butter, continuing to stir until mixture becomes thick and creamy. Season with salt and pepper and evenly fold in lobster mixture. Serve immediately.

Apple Butter

32 ounces green apples, peeled, cored, sliced and pureed
1 ½ teaspoons ground cinnamon
½ teaspoon ground cloves
½ teaspoon ground allspice

Combine all ingredients. Place in saucepan. Cook uncovered over low heat at least 1 hour to thicken and blend flavors. Pour into covered container and refrigerate. Use as a spread.

Western Omelet

3 eggs
¼ cup ham, minced
2 tablespoons onion, chopped
2 tablespoons green pepper, chopped
1 tablespoon butter

Mix eggs briefly and add in ham, onion and pepper. Heat butter in a small skillet and quickly pour in eggs mixture, stirring lightly until set on bottom. Let stand over heat a few seconds to lightly brown bottom, fold in half and season with salt and pepper to taste.

Breakfast Sausage

3 pounds fresh pork shoulder, trimmed
1 small onion, sliced
4 garlic cloves
2 teaspoons sage, crumbled
1 teaspoon savory, crumbled
2 teaspoons salt; ½ teaspoon pepper
6 tablespoons almond milk

Trim pork of all fat and cut into 1½-inch cubes. Freeze for 30 minutes. In meat grinder or food processor, grind pork, add onion and garlic and grind once more. Remove to a large bowl and blend in spices. Stir in milk, 1 tablespoon at a time. Cover and chill for an hour.

Form into 16 patties and cover, refrigerating for a day to marry flavors. Use within two days, or wrap in airtight paper for freezing. To serve, fry over medium heat until browned and cooked through.

Zucchini & Eggs

2 teaspoons olive oil
1 zucchini, sliced
1 egg, beaten
salt and pepper to taste

Heat a small skillet over medium heat. Add oil and sauté zucchini until tender. Spread out in an even layer and pour beaten egg evenly over top. Cook until egg is firm, seasoning with salt and pepper to taste.

Grapefruit Crunch

8 red grapefruit sections
2 tablespoons yogurt
1 tablespoon almonds, toasted and chopped

Arrange grapefruit sections in a shallow bowl. Top with yogurt and sprinkle with almonds.

Strawberry Yogurt

4 cups strawberries
2 cups plain yogurt
4 tablespoons almonds, toasted and chopped

Slice strawberries in half. Divide strawberries between 4 individual bowls. Top each bowl with ½ cup yogurt. Top each bowl with 1 tablespoon of almonds.

Salads
&
Dressings

Salads & Dressings

Whether you enjoy being in the kitchen or not, salads may become your best friend, as they've been mine since 33 years ago. Easy to put together, light and great tasting, salads break up the monotony of "mono-meals" like meat and eggs. Another benefit to salads is that they make eating out easy. Most restaurants will substitute extra avocado or egg on their salads in place of mushrooms or corn. You will also learn that there are plenty of ways to be creative with left over *Initial Phase* foods — throw them all together and call the result a SALAD!

Jicama Salad

2 large beets, rinsed
2 quarts mixed baby lettuces (washed and dried = 3 cups)
jicama, peeled and diced
2 tablespoons lime juice
2 to 4 tablespoons olive oil
salt & fresh-ground pepper to taste
1/3 cup toasted mixed nuts

Place beets in a pan, cover with water and bring to a boil. Cover pan and simmer over low heat for 40 to 50 minutes, or until beets are tender. Allow to cool. Run cold water over beets, slip off their skins and cut them into wedges.

In a large bowl, toss lettuces and jicama. In a small bowl, whisk together lime juice, oil, salt and pepper. Pour over greens mixture and toss thoroughly. Adjust seasoning to taste and serve topped with beets and mixed nuts.

Makes 4 servings.

Artichoke Heart Salad

4 medium-sized or 8 small artichokes
2 tablespoons strained fresh lemon juice
salt and fresh-ground pepper, to taste
5 to 6 tablespoons extra-virgin olive oil
2 teaspoons fresh thyme (1 teaspoon dried)
½ to 1 teaspoon minced jalapeño pepper (or to taste)
1 to 2 teaspoons chopped fresh Italian parsley

For the dressing, whisk lemon juice with salt and pepper. Continue to whisk while adding oil, thyme and jalapeño pepper. Adjust seasoning to taste. Before using, whisk dressing once more and add chopped parsley.

To trim artichokes, cut off top inch of large artichokes and ½ inch from small ones. Trim spikes from tips of leaves with scissors.

Place artichokes in a large saucepan of boiling, salted water. To keep artichokes submerged, cover with a lid of slightly smaller diameter than that of the pan. Cook over medium heat, until a leaf can be easily pulled out. Medium-sized artichokes require about 30 minutes, while small ones take 15 to 20 minutes.

Using tongs, remove artichokes from water, turn them upside down, and drain thoroughly. Either cover to keep warm or let cook and serve at room temperature or chilled. Serve with dressing on the side.

Makes 4 servings.

Spicy Bell Pepper Salad

4 to 6 tablespoons of olive oil
4 large red, green, or yellow bell peppers
3 to 4 jalapeño peppers, or 6 to 8 Serrano peppers
salt to taste

Slice bell peppers into 1/3-inch strips. Remove the seeds and ribs of the jalapeño peppers and finely dice them. Heat oil in a large skillet or sauté pan, add bell peppers and sauté over medium-low heat, stirring occasionally, about 15 minutes or until peppers are nearly tender. Reduce heat as necessary, to prevent peppers from browning. Add jalapeño peppers and cook over low heat, stirring often about 5 minutes or until bell peppers are completely tender. If jalapeños begin to brown, add 2 to 3 tablespoons water. Season with salt and serve chilled.

Makes 4-6 servings.

Jami's Green Salad

1 package fresh leaf spinach
½ cup diced green onions
2 hard-boiled eggs, diced
½ cup uncured bacon, cooked and crumbled
olive oil, grape seed oil or lemon juice to taste
sea salt and pepper to taste

Combine all ingredients and serve. *Makes 4-6 servings.*

Colorful Salad

1½ to 2 cups of romaine lettuce, cut into strips
1 medium cucumber, peeled and diced
½ red bell pepper, diced
½ cup sliced black olives
½ cup finely shredded red cabbage
2 medium or large tomatoes, diced
1 green onion, white and green parts, chopped
1 to 2 tablespoons extra-virgin olive oil
1 to 2 tablespoons strained fresh lemon juice
salt and fresh-ground pepper to taste

In a large bowl, combine lettuce, cucumber, bell pepper, black olives and cabbage. Add tomato and onion and mix gently. Just before serving, toss with olive oil, lemon juice, salt and pepper. Mix gently but thoroughly.

Makes 4 servings.

Spinach Salad

4 cups tightly packed spinach leaves, rinsed and chopped
2 to 3 tablespoons olive oil
2 white onions, halved and thinly sliced
3 large cloves garlic, chopped
1 cup plain yogurt
salt, fresh-ground pepper and cayenne pepper, to taste

Bring about 1 inch of water to a boil in a sauté pan. Add spinach, cover, and return to a boil. Cook over medium heat, stirring often, about 3 minutes or until wilted. Drain in a colander, rinse with cold water then drain again. Press gently to remove excess water.

Dry sauté pan, add oil and heat. Add onion and sauté over medium-low heat for about 7 minutes or until golden-brown. Add garlic and sauté for another minute. Return spinach to pan and sauté for 2 minutes. Transfer mixture to a bowl and allow it to cool.

Stir yogurt in a bowl until it smoothens. Add spinach mixture and mix gently. Season with salt, pepper and cayenne, and serve cold.

Makes 4 servings.

Olive & Tomato Salad

2 tablespoons fresh lemon juice, strained
¼ teaspoon hot red pepper flakes (or adjust to taste)
½ teaspoon dried thyme
1 cup black olives, pitted
1 pound ripe tomatoes, finely diced
¼ cup chopped green onion
¼ cup chopped fresh Italian parsley
fresh-ground pepper, to taste

Combine lemon juice, pepper flakes and thyme in a serving bowl. Add olives, tomatoes, green onion and parsley. Season with pepper. Refrigerate in a covered container until ready to serve.

Makes 4 servings.

Eggplant & Bell Pepper Salad

grilled and served with sun-dried tomatoes

2 Japanese, Chinese, or small Italian eggplants
3 tablespoons extra-virgin olive oil (save a little for brushing)
1 red bell pepper, halved and cored
salt and fresh-ground pepper to taste
1 yellow or green bell pepper, halved and cored
8 cups spinach leaves
1½ to 2 tablespoons strained fresh lemon juice
1 teaspoon fresh thyme *(or ½ teaspoon dried)*
2 tablespoons slivered, fresh basil *(optional)*
6 oil-packed sun-dried tomatoes, halved

Slice 2 eggplants horizontally into ½ inch slices. Brush eggplant slices lightly with oil on both sides and sprinkle with salt and pepper. Grill or broil 5 to 7 minutes on each side or until tender. Remove and allow to cool.

Lay pepper slices on grill or broiler with their skin sides down. Grill or broil about 5 minutes or until pepper skins begin to blister. Remove peppers to a bowl, cover and let stand 10 minutes. Pull off their skins.

Cut peppers into strips about 1/3-inch wide. Dice eggplants. Combine with spinach in a large bowl.

For dressing, in a small bowl whisk 3 tablespoons of oil with lemon juice, thyme, salt, and pepper. Add to salad mixture and toss gently. Mix in basil, adjusting seasoning as necessary. Top with sun-dried tomatoes.

Makes 6 servings.

Springtime Salad

4 medium tomatoes (or 8 to 12 plum tomatoes), diced
1 long cucumber (or 2 small cucumbers) peeled and diced
¼ to ½ sweet white onion, minced
8 small red radishes, diced
1/3 cup chopped fresh Italian parsley
1 cup coarsely chopped arugula (optional)
2 to 3 tablespoons extra-virgin olive oil
1 to 2 tablespoons strained fresh lemon juice
salt and fresh-ground pepper, to taste

Mix tomatoes, cucumber, radishes, onion, parsley, and arugula (if using) in a glass bowl. Add olive oil, lemon juice, salt and pepper. Serve cool or chilled.

Makes 8 servings.

California-style Salad

½ cup cucumber, diced
8 plum tomatoes, or 4 medium tomatoes, diced
½ cup chopped red, white, or sweet onion
1 small red, orange, or yellow bell pepper, diced
1 cup peeled jicama, finely diced
3 to 4 teaspoons chopped fresh Italian parsley
1 to 2 tablespoons extra-virgin olive oil
1 to 2 tablespoons strained fresh lemon juice
salt and fresh-ground pepper, to taste

Toss cucumbers, tomato, onion, peppers, Jicama, and parsley in a bowl. Add oil, lemon juice, and salt and pepper. Serve chilled or at room temperature. *Makes 4 servings.*

Spinach & Feta Cheese Salad

¾ pound fresh spinach (1 medium bunch), or a 10 oz. bag of rinsed spinach leaves

½ small fennel bulb, cut into slender sticks (optional)

2 thin slices of red onion, halved and then separated into half moons

1 large cucumber, halved and cut into thin slices

2 to 3 tablespoons fresh lemon juice, strained

2 medium tomatoes, cut into eight wedges

½ cup crumbled feta cheese

2 to 3 tablespoons of extra-virgin olive oil

salt and fresh-ground pepper, to taste

8 to 12 black olives (optional)

If using fresh, uncut spinach, remove stems and any wilted leaves and wash thoroughly. Dry spinach well and tear any large leaves into two to three pieces.

In a large bowl, toss together spinach, red onion, fennel (if using), and cucumber. Add olive oil, lemon juice, salt and pepper and toss. Adjust seasoning to taste. Spoon salads onto plates or a shallow serving dish, arranging tomato wedges around the edges. Sprinkle with feta cheese and garnish with olives.

Makes 4 servings.

Everyday Salad

4 medium-sized tomatoes, cut into ½-inch dice
1 medium-sized cucumber
¼ cup minced green onion

1 to 2 tablespoons extra-virgin olive oil
1 to 2 tablespoons fresh lemon juice, strained
salt and fresh-ground pepper to taste

Peel cucumber and cut into ½-inch sized dice. Mix together with tomatoes and green onion in a bowl. Add oil, lemon juice, salt and pepper. Serve cool or at room temperature.
Makes 4 servings.

Garlic & Cumin Dressed Salad

1 small clove of garlic, finely chopped
½ teaspoon paprika
½ teaspoon ground cumin
3 tablespoons extra-virgin olive oil
1 tablespoons strained fresh lemon juice
salt and fresh-ground pepper, to taste
cayenne pepper, to taste
4 to 6 cups lettuce, cut into bite-sized pieces
(use any type of lettuces, from basic iceberg to romaine)
½ cup red or white onion, quartered, sliced and slivered
¼ cup chopped fresh Italian parsley (optional)
2 large or 4 medium tomatoes cut into wedges

For dressing, combine garlic, cumin, paprika, cayenne in a small bowl. Stir in lemon juicc. Slowly whisk in olive oil. Add salt and pepper to taste.

Combine lettuce, onion slivers, and parsley (if using) in a bowl. Add about three quarters of the dressing and toss gently. Transfer to a platter and top with tomato wedges. Sprinkle with remaining dressing and serve. *Makes 4 to 6 servings.*

Spice Medley Salad

1 small clove garlic, finely minced or pressed
1 to 2 tablespoons of extra-virgin olive oil
1 tablespoon fresh lemon juice, strained
salt and fresh-ground pepper to taste
cayenne pepper to taste
1 large cucumber, halved and thinly sliced
1 green or yellow bell pepper, cut into strips
1 red bell pepper, cut into strips
3 tablespoons fresh mint, coarsely chopped
fresh mint sprigs

For dressing, in a small bowl whisk together garlic, lemon juice, oil, salt, pepper and cayenne.

In a shallow serving bowl, combine cucumber slices and pepper strips. Add dressing to salad and toss well. Just before serving, add mint and toss once more. Serve garnished with mint sprigs.

Makes 4 servings.

Carrot & Radish Salad

For an eye-catching salad, when preparing the carrots and radishes hold them almost parallel to the grater to get attractive, long shreds.

2 cups coarsely grated radish
2 cups coarsely grated carrot
1 green onion, white and green parts, chopped
2 to 3 tablespoons olive oil
2 tablespoons strained fresh lemon juice
salt and fresh-ground pepper, to taste

With a fork, lightly mix grated vegetables with green onion, oil, and lemon juice in a bowl. Season with salt and pepper. Serve cold or room temperature.

Makes 4-6 servings.

Spicy Carrot Salad

If you are used to carrots always being flavored with sweet seasoning, this salad will be a pleasant surprise.

2 to 3 tablespoons strained fresh lemon juice
1 small clove garlic, finely minced or pressed
2 to 3 tablespoons extra-virgin olive oil
¼ teaspoon hot red pepper flakes
1 teaspoon paprika
½ teaspoon ground cumin
1½ pounds medium carrots, sliced into ¼-inch rounds
¼ cup chopped fresh Italian parsley
salt and cayenne pepper to taste

For dressing, whisk together lemon juice, garlic, oil, salt, hot red pepper flakes, paprika and cumin in a medium-sized bowl.

Place carrots in a saucepan, cover with water, add salt and bring to a boil. Simmer about 7 minutes or until carrots are just tender. Drain and transfer warm carrots to a bowl of dressing and mix gently.

Add parsley just before serving. Adjust seasoning to taste, adding more salt and cayenne as needed. Serve hot, warm or chilled.

Makes 4-6 servings.

Garlicky Beet Salad

2 pounds of beets of about 1½ inch in diameter
3 to 4 large cloves of garlic, pressed or finely minced
1 white or red onion, grated (any mild variety will do)
2 tablespoons apple cider vinegar
1 tablespoon olive oil
salt and fresh-ground pepper to taste

Rinse beets, taking care not to pierce their skins. Place in a large saucepan, cover with water and bring to a boil. Cover and simmer over low heat for 40-50 minutes or until tender. Allow to cool. Rinse once more under cold water. Slip off skins and grate beets using the large holes of a grater. Combine grated beet with garlic, onion, vinegar, oil, salt and pepper. Cover and refrigerate overnight to allow flavors to blend. Adjust seasoning and serve chilled. *Makes 8 servings*.

Colorful Cucumber Salad

6 cups mixed baby greens, rinsed and dried thoroughly
1½ cups cucumber, halved lengthwise and sliced thin
1 tablespoon strained fresh lemon juice
2 to 3 tablespoons extra-virgin olive oil
salt and fresh-ground pepper to taste
1/3 cup high quality black olives
½ to 1 cup coarsely crumbled feta cheese

Place greens in a bowl. Add cucumber, lemon juice, 2 tablespoons oil, salt and pepper. Toss thoroughly. Taste and add more oil if desired. Scatter olives and cheese over the top and serve.

Makes 4 servings.

Zucchini Salad

This easy-to-make salad features zucchini cooked in a spicy tomato-garlic dressing and topped with fresh cilantro.

1 ½ pounds zucchini, quartered lengthwise and diced
2 large cloves garlic, minced
¼ teaspoon hot red pepper flakes
2 tablespoons extra-virgin olive oil
¼ cup water
salt and fresh-ground black pepper to taste
1 tablespoon tomato paste
1 teaspoon ground cumin
cayenne pepper, to taste
1 green onion, chopped
1 to 2 tablespoons strained fresh lemon juice
1 to 2 tablespoons chopped fresh cilantro

Place zucchini in a large skillet or sauté pan with garlic, pepper flakes, oil, and water. Sprinkle with salt and pepper and bring to a boil. Cook uncovered over medium-high heat, stirring often, for about 5 minutes or until zucchini is crisp-tender and most of liquid has evaporated. Add tomato paste, cumin, and cayenne and stir over low heat for 30 seconds. Remove from heat and add onion and lemon juice. Adjust seasoning to taste. Sprinkle with cilantro and serve warm or cool.

Makes 4-5 servings.

Smoked Salmon Salad

1 cup sour cream

2 cups plain yogurt

1 green onion, white and green parts, finely chopped *(reserve a tablespoon for garnish)*

2 tablespoon chopped fresh dill (dried 1 teaspoon)

salt and fresh-ground pepper to taste

cayenne pepper to taste

2 large cucumbers, thinly sliced

4 ounces smoked salmon, cut into thin strips (reserve a few for garnish)

Mix sour cream and yogurt in a bowl, add unreserved green onion, dill, salt, pepper, and cayenne pepper. Mix well. Put cucumber in a shallow serving bowl. Add sour cream mixture and blend gently. Stir in the larger amount of salmon, taste and adjust seasoning. Serve cold and garnish with reserved salmon and green onions. *Makes 6-8 servings.*

Goat Cheese & Walnut Salad

with spinach and bell peppers

½ red bell pepper
½ yellow bell pepper
6 cups rinsed spinach leaves
1½ tablespoons extra-virgin olive oil
2¼ teaspoon apple-cider vinegar
¼ teaspoon dried thyme
salt and fresh-ground pepper, to taste

¼ cup walnut pieces, toasted
¼ to ½ cup crumbled goat cheese

Cut peppers into strips of about 1/3 inch in width, slicing in half if too long. Combine with spinach in a large bowl. For dressing, whisk oil, vinegar and thyme in a small bowl. Toss with bell peppers and spinach and season with salt and pepper. Top with walnuts and goat's cheese and serve.

Makes 4 servings.

Yogurt and Mint Salad

with cucumber and tomatoes

2 cups plain yogurt
salt and fresh-ground pepper to taste
pinch of cayenne pepper
1 tablespoon chopped fresh mint (dried 1 teaspoon)
1 green onion, chopped
1 cucumber, finely diced
4 small or medium-sized tomatoes, diced

Mix yogurt with salt, pepper and cayenne. Lightly stir in mint, onion, cucumber, and tomatoes. Adjust seasoning and refrigerate. Serve cold.

Makes 4 servings.

Spicy Cauliflower Salad

2 pounds cauliflower
2 teaspoons ground cumin
2 tablespoons strained fresh lemon juice
½ teaspoon paprika
cayenne pepper to taste
1 tablespoon water (filtered)
3 tablespoons olive oil
1 red bell pepper, diced
1/3 cup chopped red onion
¼ cup chopped fresh cilantro
salt and fresh-ground pepper to taste

Divide cauliflower into medium-sized florets. Peel stems and slice them. Cook cauliflower in a large pan of boiling salted water uncovered over high heat for about 7 minutes, or until crisp--tender. Drain, rinse with cold water, and drain again.

In a bowl large enough to contain the cauliflower, whisk lemon juice with cumin, paprika, cayenne and water. Add olive oil and whisk again. Add cauliflower, bell pepper, onion and 3 tablespoons cilantro. Gently toss to mix. Season with salt and pepper, sprinkle with remaining chopped cilantro and serve at room temperature.

Makes 4 servings.

Okra Salad

When cooked at all, most vegetables are boiled or steamed before being added to a salad. Okra instead seems to taste better sautéed, then simmered with a small amount of water added. The vegetable is best served with a simple dressing, such as the lemon juice, coriander seed, garlic and cilantro combination featured in this recipe.

3 tablespoons extra-virgin olive oil
1 pound fresh okra, rinsed and patted dry, caps trimmed
salt and fresh-ground pepper to taste
1/4 cup water
1/4 cup chopped red onion
2 tablespoon strained fresh lemon
1 medium-sized clove of garlic, very finely minced
1/4 teaspoon ground coriander
cayenne pepper to taste
2 tablespoons fresh cilantro, chopped

Heat 2 tablespoons of oil in a large sauté pan; add okra and sauté 2 minutes over medium heat, stirring lightly. Sprinkle with salt and pepper. Add water, cover and cook over low heat for about 7 minutes or until just tender, shaking pan occasionally and adding water only if needed. Remove okra gently to a shallow serving dish. Add onion and mix carefully.

For the dressing, combine another tablespoon of oil, lemon juice, garlic, coriander, cayenne, salt and pepper in a bowl and pour over okra. Sprinkle with cilantro and serve chilled or at room temperature.

Makes 4 servings.

Doug's Favorite Meal!

This quick and easy dish is Doug Kaufmann's favorite.

1 tomato, diced
1 small onion, diced
1 cucumber, diced
1 avocado, diced
½ cup black olives, diced
3 hard boiled eggs (sliced)
smoked salmon or cubes of beef summer sausage
olive oil (or grape seed oil)
5 tablespoons freshly-squeezed lemon juice

Dice and combine first five ingredients, add sliced boiled eggs and smoked salmon. Top with olive oil and freshly squeezed lemon juice. *Makes 2 servings.*

Bell Pepper & Tomato Salad

Fresh green pepper, cucumber and tomato blend perfectly with this recipe's slightly garlicky lemon dressing. This salad can be prepared in the morning for serving later the same day.

Salad

2 large fresh tomatoes
1 large green pepper
1 cucumber, peeled and seeded
4 green onions, including tops

Dressing

3 tablespoons fresh lemon juice
1 small clove of garlic, pressed

½ teaspoon salt
¼ teaspoon coarsely cracked pepper
3 tablespoon olive oil
¼ cup minced parsley
minced parsley or mint sprigs for garnish

Dip tomatoes in boiling water and peel, de-seed and chop them. De-seed and chop the green pepper — pieces should be no larger than ½ inch. Chop the cucumber and set it aside.

For the dressing, whisk together lemon juice, garlic, salt, pepper and olive oil. Fold in the chopped tomatoes, green pepper, cucumber, green onions and parsley. Spoon into a glass serving bowl, cover and chill for at least an hour. Garnish with parsley or mint sprigs and serve.

Makes 4 servings.

Tuna Salad

½ cup plain yogurt
1 tablespoon lemon juice
¼ teaspoon salt or Mrs. Dash
one 12-ounce can of tuna, crumbled
1 small onion, sliced
1 stalk celery, coarsely chopped
1 carrot, coarsely chopped
1 small tomato, diced
1 jalapeño pepper, chopped (optional)

Lightly blend all ingredients. Chill and serve with slices, chunks, or cubes of a variety of raw vegetables.

Makes approximately 1½ cups.

Coleslaw

This colorful coleslaw is dressed with a slightly sweet vinaigrette dressing. For a different taste, add a little fresh-crushed garlic. This slaw will keep for several days in the refrigerator, and it goes well with just about any grilled or baked meat.

Salad

1 small head cabbage, shredded
1 small white onion, chopped
1 green pepper, chopped
1 red pepper, chopped
1 small carrot, grated
3 tablespoons minced parsley

Dressing

½ cup apple cider vinegar
2 to 3 drops of liquid Stevia
½ teaspoon salt
¼ teaspoon white pepper
½ cup salad oil

Combine cabbage, onion, green and red peppers, carrot, and parsley. Toss to mix. For dressing, combine the apple cider vinegar, stevia, salt, pepper and oil in a jar or shaker. Shake to blend and pour over slaw. Cover and chill. Gently toss just prior to serving.

Makes 4 servings.

Beet & Walnut Salad

Head of lettuce
3 beets; cooked and peeled
2 Granny Smith apples, peeled and cored
½ cup walnuts
1/3 cup thinly sliced scallions
1/3 cup creamy herb dressing
½ cup goat cheese

Cube the beets and the apples and mix together in a bowl with the cheese, walnuts and scallions. Drizzle dressing over and stir to coat. Serve on a bed of lettuce.

Herb Salad

2 cups flat-leaf parsley leaves
1 cup basil leaves
½ cup tarragon leaves
½ cup chives
¾ cup baby arugula leaves
¾ cup chervil sprigs
½ cup small cilantro sprigs
grapeseed oil to taste
lemon juice to taste
salt and pepper to taste

Wash the leaves gently and dry. Lightly toss the leaves in a scant amount of grapeseed oil (or your favorite oil) or fresh lemon juice. Season with salt and pepper.

Doug Kaufmann

Lobster & Avocado Salad

with grapefruit segments

One (1 1/4 to 1 1/2 pound) live lobster
2 teaspoons finely chopped shallot
1 tablespoon fresh lemon juice
2 tablespoons olive oil
1 pink grapefruit
1 firm avocado
1 ounce baby arugula
1/4 tablespoon salt

Plunge lobster head-first into an 8-quart pot of boiling salted, water. Cook covered over high heat 6 minutes (for 1 1/4 pound lobster) or 7 minutes (for 1 1/2 pound lobster). Transfer with tongs to sink to drain. When lobster is cool enough to handle, remove meat from tail and claws, keeping it intact. Discard tomalley, any roe, and shells. Cover and chill lobster meat for least an hour.

While lobster chills, stir together shallot, lemon juice, and salt in a small bowl and let stand at room temperature for 30 minutes. Whisk in oil.

Cut peel, including all white pith, from grapefruit. Cut segments free from membranes and transfer to paper towels to drain. Halve avocado, discard pit and scoop out meat with a soup spoon. Cut halves in half once more and then cut them crosswise to make 1/3 inch thick slices.

Cut lobster meat crosswise into 1/2 inch thick slices. Divide avocado and all of lobster meat between 2 salad plates and arrange grapefruit around them. Top with arugula, drizzle with dressing, sprinkle lightly with salt and serve.

Herb Dressing

Great with green salads, or as a dip for veggie slices, chunks or cubes.

1 teaspoon dry mustard
1 teaspoon dill weed
¼ teaspoon tarragon
pinch of thyme
pinch of oregano
1 tablespoon fresh parsley, chopped
½ teaspoon sea salt
¼ teaspoon freshly ground black pepper
½ cup virgin olive oil

Stir together all ingredients except olive oil, until dry mustard is dissolved. Allow to sit for 10 minutes. Blend in olive oil, beginning with 1/3 cup and adding additional oil to taste.

Makes ½ cup.

Basic Dressing

4 tablespoons extra-virgin olive oil
1½ tablespoons lemon juice
1 medium garlic clove, crushed (optional)
salt to taste
fresh-ground pepper

Combine above ingredients in a salad bowl. Beat with a whisk until smooth and creamy. Add salad ingredients and toss.

Makes 2-3 servings.

Roasted Garlic

Preheat oven to 350 degrees. Cut about ½ inch from tip end of a whole head of garlic so that cloves are exposed. Place garlic on aluminum foil, drizzle with 1 tablespoon olive oil and seal foil around garlic. Place in baking dish and place in oven for 45-60 minutes. Allow to cool before squeezing the garlic from individual cloves.

Garlic Oil

(a variation on "Roasted Garlic," above)

After placing garlic in bowl, add enough olive oil to half-submerge the cloves. After roasting, save the oil for use in some of the salad dressing recipes in this book.

Vinaigrette

½ cup garlic oil (from roasted garlic recipe; see above)
½ cup unpasteurized apple cider vinegar

To make raspberry vinaigrette, add 1/2 cup of puréed raspberries. Filter fruit through a fine meshed sieve to remove the seeds, or leave them in as desired.

Garlic Yogurt Salad Dressing

Combine:

1 tablespoon garlic oil
1 cup yogurt
½ teaspoon salt
½ teaspoon fresh ground pepper

Raspberry Yogurt Dressing

Combine the following and top with fresh or frozen raspberries.

½ cup yogurt
1/3 cup raspberry purée with or without seeds
pinch of salt

Cucumber-Yogurt Dressing

This recipe can also be used as a spread.

Combine:

2 cups plain yogurt
1 small to medium-sized cucumber, finely grated (if organic, leave the skin on for added flavor)
1 fresh garlic clove, finely chopped
juice of half a lemon
salt to taste

Avocado Dressing

1 ripe avocado (medium to large)
1 medium cucumber, peeled and cut into chunks
2 teaspoons dried dill
salt to taste
1 tablespoon lime juice
2 tablespoons extra-virgin olive oil

Measure ingredients in blender container and blend for a few seconds, your dressing will be a smooth, thick cream.

Makes 1½ cups.

Herb Garlic Dressing

This recipe is big enough to serve at parties.

4½ cups extra-virgin olive oil
¾ cup fresh lemon juice
10 medium garlic cloves (garlic powder use ¼ cup)
3 teaspoons paprika
2 teaspoons dried basil
2 teaspoons dried mint
2 teaspoons dried thyme
1 teaspoon dried chervil (or dried parsley)
¼ cup seasoned salt

Measure half the ingredients in a blender and blend until smooth and creamy, taking care that garlic breaks down entirely. Measure the second half of the ingredients into the blender and repeat. *Serves 40.*

Lemon Vinaigrette

½ cup extra-virgin olive oil
3 tablespoons lemon juice
1 tablespoon fresh thyme (dried, 1 teaspoon)
1 tablespoon fresh dill
1 tablespoon fresh chives
salt to taste
fresh-ground pepper to taste

Blend ingredients in a blender for a few seconds.
Makes ¾ cup.

Salad Greens Glossary

Produce departments carry so many types of greens that salad making can be one endless adventure. The following should make it easier to pick out some new greens next time you shop.

ARUGULA

Also called rocket, arugula is a slightly bitter green with an assertive, peppery mustard flavor. It's sold in small bunches with roots attached. Look for a bunch with fresh, bright green leaves. Arugula leaves tend to hold a lot of grit so be sure to rinse the bunch well just before using.

BELGIAN ENDIVE

These small, torpedo-shaped tight heads of white leaves have a slightly bitter flavor. The sturdy leaves are often used individually to hold an appetizer serving. Only the leaf tips have pale color (typically yellow-green), because Belgian endive is grown in total darkness. Once exposed to light, the leaves turn too green and the bitterness intensifies. Buy crisp, firmly packed pale heads.

BIBB

Bibb lettuce forms a small round head with loosely packed soft leaves. The leaves are usually pale green and have a delicate sweet flavor. Since Bibb is in the butterhead family, it's often called just butterhead or butter lettuce.

BOSTON

Similar to Bibb lettuce in flavor, texture, and appearance, Boston lettuce is slightly larger.

BUTTERHEAD

Boston and Bibb are two well-known lettuces in this family. They have small, round, loosely formed heads. The leaves are quite tender and require gentle care when handling.

CURLY ENDIVE

This endive grows in loose heads with lacy green leaves that curl at the tips. Curly endive leaves have a prickly texture and a slightly bitter taste. These sharp greens blend well with other milder greens.

DANDELION GREENS

These jagged-edged greens grow wild and are also farmed. The leaves have a tangy, bitter flavor. Dandelion greens are at their prime in early spring. Wash the bright green, tender leaves well and refrigerate them up to five days. Enjoy them fresh in a salad or sautéed like spinach.

ENDIVE

There are three main varieties of endive-Belgian endive, curly endive, and escarole.

ESCAROLE

The mildest member of the endive family, escarole has broad, slightly curved green leaves. It's available year-round and will keep several days in the refrigerator. Choose a fresh head with healthy-looking leaves.

GREEN AND RED LEAF LETTUCE

These leaf lettuces have large flaring leaves that grow in loose bunches rather than tight heads. The green leaf variety is a vivid green; the red leaf variety is green with red tips. Leaf lettuce is crisp when cold, but wilts rather quickly. Plant to store it only a few days in the refrigerator.

ICEBERG

Probably the most common lettuce around, iceberg is crisp, mild in flavor, readily available, and keeps up to a week in the refrigerator. It's a good background lettuce when making a mixed green salad.

KALE AND ORNAMENTAL KALE

A member of the cabbage family, kale is easily identifiable by its frilly edges. It has dark green leaves and a mild cabbage flavor. Fresh kale is at its peak from fall through spring. The center stalk is tough so be sure to remove it before cooking. Kale is actually highly nutritious; it's a rich source of vitamin C and calcium. Use kale within three days of purchase. Ornamental varieties are quite beautiful; they can be lavender, deep purple, yellow-green, and white. Ornamental kale has a slightly bitter taste and fairly crisp texture. It's commonly used as a garnish.

MESCLUN

Also called gourmet salad mix in some markets, mesclun is simply a mixture of tender, young salad greens. It can include green like arugula, dandelion, sorrel, and oakleaf. Wash the tender mix with care and blot dry before using.

NAPA CABBAGE

This Chinese cabbage has tall and crinkly, thick-veined leaves that are a pale yellow-green color. Unlike the strongly flavored waxy leaves of a common round head of cabbage, napa cabbage has a delicate, clean taste and crisp bite. It's available year round and is good when eaten raw, sauteed, or braised.

OAKLEAF

This is a popular small, tender leaf lettuce with red-tipped leaves and a nutty, mild flavor.

RADICCHIO

A tight head of radicchio is easy to identify. With its wine-red, cup-shaped leaves radicchio makes a beautiful salad when blended with other greens. Radicchio has a slightly tangy flavor. Store it up to a week in the refrigerator. It's available all year long.

ROMAINE

Romaine is an elongated bunch of greens with coarse, crisp leaves and heavy ribs. Cut out and discard tough ribs before serving. Romaine adds crunch to tossed salads and is famous in Caesar Salads.

SORREL

Resembling fresh spinach, sorrel leaves are bright green with sturdy stems. Sorrel ranges in length from 2 to 12 inches. Use it raw in salads or briefly sauteed like fresh spinach. Trim or tear tough stems.

SPINACH

Spinach has vivid green leaves that are curly or smooth. Fresh spinach is available year-round. Its leaves tend to be gritty, so rinse spinach well and blot dry before using. Trim or tear off tough stems. Fresh spinach can be found commonly packaged in 10-ounce bags. You might still want to rinse and tear off stems. Use spinach raw or cooked.

WATERCRESS

Watercress has a pungent, peppery bite to it and is sold in small bundles. Its dark green leaves are small and crisp. Wash and shake watercress dry just before serving.

Soups

Soups

There is nothing like a bowl of hot soup on a cold day! We've tried to be especially creative with this section's choices, including everything from cucumber soup to a good old bowl of Texas Chili. Eating a variety of foods while on the diet is not only enjoyable — it will help you stay the course.

Yogurt & Avocado Soup

When preparing this in advance, mash the entire avocado and combine it with the soup — the yogurt will prevent the avocado from darkening. Otherwise, mash half the avocado and save the rest for garnishing.

1 large garlic clove, minced
¼ cup chopped fresh mint
1 very ripe avocado
5 cups plain yogurt
1 long cucumber
1 teaspoon salt; cayenne pepper to taste
strained fresh lemon juice to taste
small fresh mint sprigs

In a large bowl, mash pitted and skinned avocado together with garlic and mint. Add yogurt and blend thoroughly.

Peel cucumber, quarter it lengthwise, cut it into thin slices and fold it into yogurt mixture. Add cayenne, adjust seasoning to taste and then add lemon juice. Refrigerate soup for at least 15 minutes and up to 4 hours.

If you used only half the avocado, slice or dice the remaining half for use in garnishing the soup. Sprinkle soup lightly with cayenne, garnish with small sprigs of mint and serve cold.

Makes 6 servings.

No-mess Pumpkin Soup

Although this easy soup begins with canned pumpkin, it's so robust and thick that it tastes as if it were made from scratch.

one 15-ounce can of pure pumpkin
2 cups chicken stock
½ cup goat's milk
1 teaspoon curry powder
salt and fresh-ground black pepper to taste
snipped, fresh chives for garnish

In a medium saucepan, combine the pumpkin and chicken stock. Whisk to blend, then whisk in the milk and curry powder. Cook over medium heat for about 10 minutes, until steaming, taking care not to boil. Season with salt and pepper and keep warm over low heat until ready to serve. Ladle 1 cup into bowls and garnish with chives.

Makes 4 servings.

Cold Cucumber-Tomato Soup

with herbs and yogurt

Garlic gives the soup its subtle kick, balanced by the fresh flavor of the herbs.

1 small clove garlic, pressed or finely minced
½ teaspoon salt, or to taste
6 cups plain yogurt
pinch of cayenne pepper
½ pound cucumbers, halved lengthwise and sliced thin
½ pound ripe tomatoes, diced finely (reserve 1/3 cup)

1 tablespoon chopped fresh dill
2 tablespoons minced fresh Italian parsley
2 tablespoons chopped fresh chives

Using the back of a spoon, mash garlic and salt together in a large bowl. Stir in yogurt and cayenne pepper, blending thoroughly. Add cucumbers and most of the tomatoes, folding them gently into the yogurt mixture. Adjust seasoning to taste. Refrigerate at least 15 minutes or up to 6 hours prior to serving.

Just before serving, stir in dill, parsley and a tablespoon of the chives. Serve soup garnished with reserved, diced tomatoes and the remaining chives.

Makes 6 servings.

Cucumber Soup

2 cucumbers
2 cups yogurt
one 10¾-ounce can of chicken broth
1 clove garlic, crushed
walnuts for garnishing

Peel cucumbers and cut into bite-size cubes. Salt heavily and set aside. Spoon yogurt into a medium casserole and stir until smooth. Stir in chicken broth and garlic. Rinse salt off cucumbers and add them to chicken broth mixture. Add salt to taste. Chill in refrigerator for several hours and garnish with chopped walnuts.

Makes 5 cups.

Meat & Vegetable Soup

This hearty soup gets its intriguing flavor from beets and cabbage cooked in beef broth. Add frankfurters or beef salami for an accent, or make the soup with red cabbage.

1 tablespoon olive oil
2 large onions, diced
4 large carrots, diced
1 parsnip or parsley root, diced
1½ pounds beef with bones (beef shanks work well)
6 cups water
1 bay leaf
3 medium-sized beets, scrubbed thoroughly with brush
3 to 4 tablespoons of tomato paste
½ small green cabbage, shredded
2 tablespoons chopped fresh parsley

Heat oil in a large saucepan over medium-heat. Add onions, carrots and parsnip and sauté for about 10 minutes, stirring often. Transfer to a bowl. Place beef in the same saucepan, cover with water and add bay leaf. Bring to a boil. Cover and cook over low heat for 30 minutes. Add beets and simmer covered for 1 hour or until beets are tender. Remove beets and slip off their skins under running water. Dice and return to saucepan.

Stir tomato paste into soup. Add sautéed vegetables, cover and simmer for 20 minutes. Add cabbage and simmer for 15 minutes or until beef and vegetables are tender. Discard bay leaf. Skim excess fat from soup (if preparing soup ahead, refrigerate, then skim off fat) and adjust seasoning. Remove beef, discard bones, dice and return to soup. Sprinkle with parsley and serve hot.

Makes 6-8 servings.

Butternut Squash with Dill Soup

This is a great soup for when you are in a hurry. Try topping it with sour cream or yogurt.

2 tablespoons olive oil
3 large onions, halved and sliced
5 cups vegetable broth
1 cup hot water
1 butternut squash (about 1¾ to 2 pounds)
½ teaspoon ground allspice
3 tablespoons chopped fresh dill (dried 2½ teaspoons)
cayenne pepper, to taste
salt and fresh-ground pepper to taste

Heat oil in Dutch oven or stew pan. Add onions and sauté over medium-high heat for about 5 minutes, or until onions begin to turn brown. Add broth and hot water. Cover and bring to a boil. Cook 10 minutes over medium-low heat.

Halve squash, place in covered bowl and microwave on high for 10 minutes or until tender. Remove and discard seeds, and scoop out flesh. Add squash, allspice and dried dill (if using dried) to soup. Cook over low heat for 7 to 10 minutes, or until vegetables are tender. If using fresh dill, stir it in at this point. Add cayenne and adjust seasoning to taste. Sprinkle with remaining dill and serve hot.

Makes 6 servings.

Squash Soup with a Spicy Flare

By using frozen, cooked squash instead of peeling, cooking, and puréeing fresh squash, you can save at least 45 minutes of preparation time. You don't have to thaw frozen ingredients —they will thaw as the soup cooks. Red jalapeño peppers give this soup its spicy, colorful accent.

3 cups vegetable stock or broth
one 12-oz. pkg frozen cooked winter squash (or fresh squash)
¼ cup chopped white onion
¼ teaspoon chopped jalapeño peppers
1 teaspoon ground cumin
¾ teaspoon paprika
½ teaspoon ground coriander
½ tablespoons fresh squeezed lime juice
salt and fresh-ground black pepper to taste
2 tablespoons chopped fresh cilantro

In a large saucepan, combine 2½ cups of the vegetable stock and the squash over high heat. In a blender, purée the remaining ½ cup of stock, the onion and the jalapeño pepper until smooth (about 5 seconds). Combine mixture with squash and stock in saucepan. Add the cumin, paprika, and coriander.

Bring to a boil, reduce heat to medium and simmer for 7 minutes, or until vegetables are heated through and steaming. Stir in lime juice and season with salt and pepper. Ladle 1 cup each into 4 soup bowls and garnish with ½ tablespoon cilantro.

Makes 4 servings.

Spicy Chicken Soup

This savory soup combines chicken with ground cumin seeds, turmeric, and plenty of black pepper.

2½ pounds chicken pieces
5 teaspoons ground cumin
2 teaspoons ground turmeric
salt and fresh-ground pepper to taste
7 cups boiling water
1 large onion, peeled
1 large tomato
3 zucchinis cut into thick slices

Place chicken in a large heavy stew pan or Dutch oven. Sprinkle with cumin, turmeric, salt, and pepper. Cook over low heat about 7 minutes, turning pieces occasionally to coat them with the spices. Add water, onion and tomato. Bring to a boil, skim foam from surface and cook covered over low heat for 1½ hours.

Add zucchini and cook another 30 minutes, or until soup is well flavored and zucchini is tender. Skim excess fat once more. Adjust seasoning to taste. Serve hot in shallow bowls.

Makes 4-6 servings.

Okra Beef Stew

Choose small okra, about 3 inches long or shorter. When okra is out of season, use frozen and cook for only 10 minutes.

3 to 4 tablespoons olive oil
1½ pounds beef chuck (1 inch pieces, patted dry)
one 14½ ounce can diced tomatoes with their juice
1½ cups beef stock or water
1 to 1¼ pounds okra
1 red or green bell pepper, cut into thin strips
3 tablespoons tomato paste
6 large cloves garlic, chopped
½ teaspoon ground allspice (or to taste)
salt to taste
juice of ½ to 1 lemon

Heat 1 tablespoon of oil in a large stew pan or Dutch oven. Add beef in batches and sauté over medium heat until browned, removing each finished batch with a slotted spoon to a plate. Add more oil if necessary between batches, increasing heat accordingly, before adding more meat and again reducing heat to medium. Return beef to pan along with any juices that have collected on plate, after pouring off any oil remaining in pan. Add tomatoes and 1 cup of stock and bring to a simmer. Cover and cook over low heat for 1½ hours. Add a few tablespoons of boiling water from time to time if pan becomes dry.

Rinse okra, place on paper towels and pat dry. Cut caps off without piercing okra. In a large, deep sauté pan, heat 2 tablespoons of oil. Add pepper strips and okra and sauté over medium heat for 5 minutes, stirring often.

Add tomato paste and remaining ½ cup stock to stew. Fold in okra and pepper mixture and bring to a simmer. Add garlic, allspice, salt and pepper. Cover and simmer without stirring for about 20 minutes or until beef and okra are tender. Add lemon juice and heat through. Adjust seasoning to taste and serve from stew pan or a deep serving dish.

Makes 4 servings.

Garlicky Carrot Soup

5 cups sliced carrots
2 cloves garlic, minced
½ cup chopped onion
1 tablespoon minced ginger root
1 teaspoon olive oil
21.5 ounces canned chicken broth (defatted) plus 1 can water
¼ cup fresh lime juice (or to taste)
yogurt for garnish

In a soup pot or large casserole dish, sauté ginger, garlic, and onion in olive oil. Add a splash of water and cook vegetables until tender. Stir in carrots, chicken broth and water and simmer until carrots are tender (about 20 minutes). Add lime juice and purée soup in blender until smooth. Serve warm or chilled. Top each soup bowl with a large dollop of yogurt, taking care to not mix the yogurt into the soup.

Makes 7 servings.

Eggplant Stew

Eggplant cooks quickly in this recipe's savory tomato sauce. The end result keeps well, reheats beautifully and can be served hot or cold. This soup works well served with roast lamb, chicken or turkey. If you use fresh eggplant with a smooth, glossy skin, peeling is unnecessary.

3 tablespoons olive oil
1 large onion, chopped
6 large cloves garlic, chopped
1 ½ pounds eggplants, unpeeled and cut into ¼-inch dice
salt and fresh-ground pepper to taste
¼ cup chopped fresh Italian parsley or cilantro
one 28-ounce can diced tomatoes
2 tablespoons tomato paste
1 bay leaf
¼ teaspoon dried hot pepper flakes or to taste
1 teaspoon dried oregano

Heat oil in a heavy stew pan or Dutch oven. Add onion and sauté over medium heat 5 minutes or until it turns golden. Stir in garlic, followed by eggplant, salt, pepper, and half the parsley. Stir over low heat for 2 to 3 minutes, until eggplant is coated with onion mixture.

Add tomatoes along with their juice, tomato paste, bay leaf, hot pepper flakes and oregano. Cook over high heat until bubbling, stirring constantly. Cover and simmer over medium-low heat for about 25 minutes, stirring often, until eggplant is tender. Discard bay leaf and adjust seasoning to taste. Sprinkle with remaining parsley and serve hot or cold.

Makes 4-5 servings.

Curried Tomato Soup

12 medium-sized (5 lbs) ripe tomatoes, halved horizontally
3 tablespoons olive oil
½ medium-sized onion, chopped
1½ teaspoons curry powder (masala curry)
1 teaspoon garlic, finely chopped
2 teaspoons apple cider vinegar
black pepper to taste (about 1/8 teaspoon)
salt to taste (about 1 teaspoon)
2 cups chicken stock or broth
2 cups water

Over low heat, grill tomatoes with cut sides up, until soft.

Combine olive oil, onion, curry powder and garlic in a saucepan over low heat. Cover, stirring occasionally until the onions soften.

Together with the onion mixture in a large saucepan, combine chicken stock/broth, water, roasted tomatoes (set aside 2-3 of these, cutting them into bite sized wedges) vinegar, salt and pepper.

Purée the above in a blender. You may want to remove the tomato seeds with a strainer, but the soup works equally well with them left in.

Return soup to sauce pan, bring to a simmer and then spoon into soup bowls. Garnish with the tomato wedges set aside earlier.

Makes 8 servings.

Ginger Squash Soup

½ cup chopped onion
6 cups butternut squash, peeled, seeded, and cut into thin slices
2 tablespoons minced ginger root
2 cans chicken broth (10¾ oz. each), defatted
4 cloves garlic
2 to 3 tablespoons of fresh lime juice
salt and fresh-ground pepper to taste

In a large soup pot, combine onion, ginger root and squash. Add broth and garlic and bring to a boil. Reduce heat, cover and simmer for about 15 minutes, until squash is tender. Purée in a blender or food processor. Return mixture to pot and stir in lime juice, salt, and pepper. Add more water, a tablespoon at a time, to lessen thickness if necessary.

Makes 7 cups.

Curried Squash Soup

This soup is rich in flavor and great as a snack or as an appetizer.

1 tablespoon olive oil
1 cup chopped carrot
1 cup chopped onion
2 teaspoons curry powder
6 cups mashed cooked acorn squash
2 cups chicken broth
6 tablespoons plain yogurt
1 tablespoon pumpkin seeds, for use as a garnish

Heat oil in medium-sized saucepan. Add carrot and onion and cook until tender (about 3 minutes). Stir in curry powder and cook for another minute.

In food processor, purée squash with chicken broth and carrot mixture in 2 batches until smooth. Return to saucepan and cook over medium heat until soup is heated through (3 to 5 minutes). Ladle evenly in to 6 soup bowls; swirl 1 tablespoon yogurt into each. Garnish each with ½ teaspoon pumpkin seeds, if desired.

Makes 6 servings.

Verde Chile Stew

"Verde" means "green," as in "Green Chile," which usually signifies large, mildly spicy Anaheim or poblano peppers.

2 pounds lean chuck roast
1½ tablespoons olive oil
½ medium-sized onion, chopped
12 large Anaheim or poblano peppers
1 teaspoon garlic salt
1 teaspoon salt
6 to 7 cups water

Roast, peel and cut peppers into pieces. Cut meat into ½ inch cubes and brown in oil in a fairly deep pan. Add onions, and brown further. Drain off excess fat and add peppers, garlic salt, salt and water. Bring to a boil and then simmer for at least 30 minutes.

Makes 6 servings.

Vegetable & Sausage Stew

1 teaspoon olive oil
1 cup finely chopped onion
6 ounces smoked sausage
½ cup diced yellow bell pepper
½ cup diced green bell pepper
4 cups (¾ inch) cubed tomato (about 1½ pounds)
2 cups diced zucchini
2 cups diced peeled eggplant (about 1 pound)
1 1/3 cups chicken broth
2 tablespoons tomato paste
½ teaspoon black pepper
¼ teaspoon salt
1 garlic clove, minced
½ cup chopped fresh parsley
1 tablespoon chopped fresh thyme

Heat oil in a Dutch oven over medium-high heat. Halve sausage lengthwise, cut into ° inch slices and add to Dutch oven together with onion and bell pepper, sautéing for 5 minutes. Add tomato and next 7 ingredients, bringing mixture to a boil. Cover, reduce heat and simmer for 35 minutes. Uncover and simmer for another 20 minutes. Stir in parsley and thyme.

Makes 4 servings.

Vegetable Medley Beef Stew

1 lb. 3 oz. of beef stew meat, cubed and broiled 2 minutes
1 cup chopped onion
4 cups beef broth
4 cups canned, crushed tomatoes
3 cups chopped carrots
1 cup chopped celery
1 cup tomato sauce
11 cups thinly shredded cabbage
1 cup cauliflower
1 cup zucchini
1 cup squash
¼ cup chopped fresh flat-leaf parsley
1½ teaspoons dried basil
2 tablespoons olive oil

Coat a large saucepan or a 5-quart Dutch oven with olive oil and heat for 1 minute. Add beef and onion and cook over medium-heat, stirring occasionally, until beef is lightly browned (about 5 minutes). Add broth, tomatoes, carrots, celery and tomato sauce, along with 4 cups of water. Bring to a boil. Reduce heat, cover partially and simmer 1 hour. Add remaining ingredients and cook until cabbage is tender, or 20 to 30 minutes. Ladle evenly into soup bowls.

Makes 10 servings.

Garden Tomato Soup

2 tablespoons of olive oil
¾ cup chopped onion
1 tablespoon chopped fresh oregano or basil
1 teaspoon chopped fresh thyme (dried ¼ teaspoon)
2 garlic cloves, chopped
5 cups diced tomato (about 2 pounds)
1½ cups water
2½ tablespoons tomato paste
¼ teaspoon salt
¼ teaspoon black pepper
fresh basil, thinly sliced (optional)

Heat olive oil in a large saucepan over medium heat. Add onion, oregano, thyme and garlic and cook for 4 minutes, stirring frequently. Stir in tomato and next 4 ingredients (water down to pepper). Bring to a boil and reduce heat, simmering for 15 minutes.

Pour half of soup into a blender or food processor. Process until smooth, and pour into a bowl. Repeat with remaining soup. Sprinkle with fresh basil, if desired, and serve hot or chilled.

Makes 5 servings.

Texas Chili

4 pounds chili-ground meat
1 large onion
2 cloves garlic
1 teaspoon ground oregano
1 teaspoon cumin seed
3 tablespoons chili powder
32 ounces of canned stewed tomatoes, crushed
or 2 lbs ripe tomatoes, diced
2 cups hot water
2 green bell peppers, chopped
3 large red and 3 large yellow sweet bell peppers, chopped
2 to 3 jalapeño peppers, to taste
salt to taste

Brown chili meat and onion in large heavy skillet. Add garlic and stir for 1 minute. Add oregano, cumin, chili powder, tomatoes and hot water. Bring to a boil, lower heat and simmer about an hour. Skim off fat. Add bell peppers, jalapeños, and salt, to taste, and cook for another 15 minutes.

Makes 9 servings.

Herbed Fish & Tomato Stew

As easy as it is colorful, this stew features fresh cod fillet.

1½ pounds cod fillets
salt to taste
coarsely ground pepper
6 to 8 green onions, thinly sliced
2 tablespoons butter
1 clove garlic, minced or pressed
1 bay leaf, crumbled
1 teaspoon dry thyme leaves
½ cup fish broth
1 pound canned tomatoes
½ lemon, thinly sliced

Wipe fish with a damp cloth, cut into serving pieces and sprinkle both sides with salt and pepper. In a deep frying pan or Dutch oven, cook onions in butter over medium heat until soft and still bright green. Add garlic, bay leaf, thyme, broth and tomatoes, along with the liquid in the can. Break tomatoes up with a fork and bring mixture to a boil. Reduce heat and simmer, uncovered, stirring occasionally until mixture thickens (10-15 minutes).

Add lemon slices and fish and cover. Simmer over low heat until fish is opaque and flakes when tested with a fork (8-10 minutes). Taste and add salt as needed. Serve fish in shallow bowls with tomato sauce spooned over.

Makes 4 servings.

Lobster & Chestnut Soup

1¾ to 2 pound live lobster
3 cups almond milk
2 cups chicken broth
1 small bay leaf
6 thyme sprigs
4 parsley sprigs
3 cups chestnuts (15 to 16 ounces)
1 tablespoon butter

Boil lobster in a pot of salted water until its shell turns bright red and the meat is opaque in center, or about 8 minutes. Drain, transfer to a large bowl and allow to cool.

Working over the same bowl in order to catch the juices, twist off claws, cut off tail and remove lobster meat from shells. Set shells aside after scraping out and discarding green tomalley. Cut the meat into ½ inch pieces, cover and chill.

Place reserved lobster shells and herbs on a double layer of cheesecloth and gather sides together into a pouch. Secure with cooking twine. Place the pouch into a large, heavy saucepan, along with almond milk, chicken broth and chestnuts. Simmer uncovered, stirring occasionally, until chestnuts are tender, about 15 minutes.

With tongs, pull pouch from mixture and carefully press against side of pan to drain liquids. Discard pouch.

Working in batches, purée soup in blender. Return soup to pot and bring to a simmer. Thin with more broth, as necessary, continuing to stir until heated through. Season with salt and pepper.

Meanwhile, melt butter in small skillet over medium heat. Add lobster meat and sauté 1 minute to heat through. Ladle soup into bowls and top with lobster meat. Sprinkle with minced, fresh chives and serve.

Beet Soup

1 bunch of beets, peeled, halved, sliced
3 stalks celery, diced
1 large onion, diced
4 carrots, sliced
½ tablespoon apple cider vinegar
8 ounces tomato juice (may use V8)
1 tablespoon lemon juice
salt and pepper to taste

Place vegetables in a large pot and cover with water. Add remaining ingredients and mix thoroughly. Simmer 2 to 2½ hours, or until beets and carrots are tender.

Sauces,
Dips
&
Appetizers

Sauces, Dips & Appetizers

Rewarding yourself for being good is one of life's pleasures! You've really followed the diet and you're noticing great results in body and mind. It's now time for eggplant caviar or roasted onion dip! Being creative keeps a smile on your face and encourages you to share new recipe ideas with your loved ones. By enjoying this section of the recipe book, you will keep your commitment to the program, thereby maintaining good health, yet you won't feel restricted on the diet!

Radishes with Whipped Goat Cheese

You can prepare this dish to accompany a main meal, or to function as an appetizer. Keep the radish leaves chilled until just before serving.

24 radishes with leaves (about 2 large bunches)
¼ cup (2 ounces) goat's cheese
1 teaspoon water
¼ teaspoon salt
¼ teaspoon ground cumin

Remove leaves from radishes, leaving 1 inch of the stems, and scrub with a brush. Wash and drain leaves and arrange them decoratively on a salad platter. Cut radishes in half lengthwise, for placement on platter with cut sides up. Combine cheese, water, salt and cumin in a small bowl; stir with a rubber spatula until smooth. Spread cheese mixture evenly over the "tops" of the radish halves and arrange them on platter.

Makes 24 servings.

Liver Paté

Take care to thoroughly brown the onions and to work the salt and pepper all the way through the liver.

1 pound chicken livers
3 tablespoons vegetable oil
2 medium-sized onions, chopped
2 large hard boiled eggs, coarsely grated
salt and fresh-ground pepper to taste
lettuce leaves and tomato slices

Preheat broiler with rack about 3 inches from heat source. Rinse livers and pat dry on paper towels, cutting off any green spots. Place livers on foil-lined broiler rack and sprinkle with salt. Broil for 3 minutes or until livers brown lightly on top. Turn them over, sprinkle once more with salt and broil another 3 or 4 minutes or until cooked through and color is no longer pink. Check by cutting with a sharp knife. Discard juice from foil and allow to cool slightly.

Heat oil in a large, heavy skillet. Spoon in onions and sauté over medium-low heat until tender and well browned, stirring often (about 15 minutes). Use a food processor to chop the liver. Add onions and chop with brief pulses until well blended. Transfer mixture to a bowl, lightly mix in eggs and season well with salt and pepper. Cover and refrigerate until ready to use (keeps up to 2 days). To serve, scoop onto lettuce leaves and garnish with tomato slices.

Makes 6-8 servings.

Smoked Whitefish Spread

8 ounces whipped cream cheese
1/3 cup smoked whitefish flakes
2 teaspoons fresh chives, chopped
2-3 tablespoons sour cream (optional)
fresh-ground black pepper to taste
cayenne pepper to taste

In a small bowl, mix cream cheese with whitefish and chives. If spread is too thick, stir in sour cream, a tablespoon at a time. Season with pepper and cayenne and refrigerate until ready to serve.

Makes 6 servings.

Smoked Salmon Spread

Soften the cream cheese at room temperature and add a few tablespoons of sour cream to give it a more spreadable consistency. Try topping with blanched asparagus tips.

1 pound whipped cream cheese
2 to 4 ounces smoked salmon, finely chopped
5 teaspoons chopped fresh chives or green onion
salt and fresh-ground pepper to taste

Mix cheese with salmon and chives in a small bowl. Add salt and pepper to taste.

Makes 8-12 servings.

Avocado Butter

Avocado takes on a buttery quality when it fully ripens, which makes it a natural for this kind of recipe.

½ cup butter, softened
½ cup mashed ripe avocado
3 tablespoons fresh lime juice
2 tablespoons minced fresh flat-leaf parsley
2 cloves garlic, minced
½ teaspoon salt.

Combine butter and avocado in a small bowl; mash with a potato masher until smooth. Add lime juice and remaining ingredients; stir well. Cover and chill until firm. If desired, shape butter mixture into small balls before serving.

Makes 1 cup.

Divine Veggie Dip

26 ounces sour cream
8 ounce cream cheese
3 tablespoon minced onion (fresh or dried)
5 tablespoons Mrs. Dash (any flavor — *salad herb* works well)
3 tablespoons seasoned salt
1 juice of lemon
2 tablespoons chili powder

Mix together well, chill and serve with fresh vegetables.

Tomato Salsa

A 4.5-ounce can of chopped green chilies (drained) can be substituted for the jalapeño.

2 cups peeled and chopped tomatoes (3 large tomatoes)
½ cup green onions, thinly sliced (about 3 onions)
1 jalapeño pepper, seeded and finely chopped
2 tablespoons lemon or lime juice
½ teaspoon salt
½ teaspoon dried oregano
1/8 teaspoon pepper

Combine all ingredients and stir well. Cover and chill for at least 3 hours.

Makes 2 cups.

Creamy Cucumber Sauce

Grated cucumber adds a nice texture to this creamy sauce.

1 medium-sized cucumber
½ cup sour cream
1 teaspoon grated onion
1 tablespoon lemon juice
½ teaspoon pepper

Peel and seed cucumber. Grate enough of the cucumber to generate ½ cup. Combine this with sour cream and remaining ingredients, stirring well. Cover and chill.

Makes 1 cup.

Roasted Pepper Sauce

2 green bell peppers
2 large red bell peppers
2 jalapeño peppers
1 tablespoon olive oil
one 28-ounce can tomatoes, drained and chopped
3 large cloves garlic, minced
¼ cup minced fresh cilantro
2 teaspoons paprika
1 teaspoon ground cumin
salt to taste
pinch of ground pepper

Preheat broiler or grill. Broil green and red bell peppers, turning every 5 minutes, until their skins are blistered and charred (about 20 minutes total). Broil jalapeño peppers, turning often, about 5 minutes. Transfer peppers to bowl and cover, or place in a plastic bag and seal. Let stand 10 minutes and then peel bell peppers and jalapeño peppers using a paring knife. Halve peppers and discard seeds and ribs. Cut bell peppers into ½ inch dice. Chop jalapeño peppers.

Heat oil in a large skillet. Add tomatoes, bell peppers, jalapeño peppers, garlic, cilantro, paprika, cumin and salt. Cook uncovered over medium heat about 20 minutes, or until sauce is thick, stirring often. Season with cayenne and serve hot or chilled.

Makes 4 servings.

Creamy Cucumber-Dill Sauce

1 medium-sized cucumber
2 cups plain yogurt
3 tablespoons chopped fresh dill (dried 2 teaspoons)
1 tablespoon fresh Italian parsley, chopped (optional)
1 green onion, white and green parts, finely chopped
salt and fresh-ground pepper to taste

Peel cucumber , cut it in half lengthwise and remove seed-filled center with a spoon. Coarsely grate cucumber. Mix yogurt, dill, parsley, if using, and onion in a medium bowl. Stir in grated cucumber. Season with salt, pepper and cayenne, mix well and serve cold.

Makes 3 cups (about 8 servings).

Mexican Rub

1/4 cup chili powder
1 tablespoon onion powder
2 teaspoons salt
1 tablespoon ground cumin
1 1/2 teaspoon dried oregano
1 teaspoon garlic powder
1 teaspoon ground red pepper

Mix all ingredients and store in an airtight container. Rub on chicken, ribs, or fish before grilling.

Makes 1/2 cup.

Eggplant Caviar

This tasty and easy-to-make appetizer spread will keep in your refrigerator for up to 2 weeks.

¼ cup butter
1 cup chopped onion
1 large eggplant, pared and diced into ½ inch pieces
1 8-ounce can of tomato sauce
1 clove garlic, minced or pressed
1 teaspoon salt
½ teaspoon freshly ground black pepper
dash hot pepper sauce
1 to 2 teaspoons fresh lemon juice
chopped fresh parsley and tomato for garnish

Melt butter in a heavy skillet and add onion and eggplant. Sauté for 2 minutes. Stir in tomato sauce and garlic. Simmer over low heat for 45 minutes, stirring occasionally, until eggplant is no longer chewy. Check to be sure no browning occurs on the bottom of pan.

When mixture is very thick and vegetables are done, remove from heat. Add salt, black pepper, hot pepper sauce and lemon juice to taste. Cover and chill. To serve, sprinkle with fresh parsley and tomato.
Makes 3 cups.

Easy Chili Seasoning Blend

Sprinkle this simple seasoning on ground beef or chicken.

3 tablespoons chili powder
1 teaspoon garlic powder
1 tablespoon salt
1 ½ teaspoons black pepper
¾ teaspoon ground red pepper

Combine all ingredients and store in an airtight container for up to 1 month.

Makes 1/3 cup.

Sautéed Onions

3 medium onions
½ cup extra virgin olive oil

Dice onions to preferred size and spoon into sauté pan. Pour in oil and stir until onions are well-covered. Cover and cook at medium temperature for 15 minutes. Turn off burner, allow onions to cool, spoon into a jar and refrigerate. Use as needed in preparing meals.

Cashew Almond Breading

1 cup cashews
1 cup almonds

Place nuts in food processor and grind them to a texture not quite as fine as flour. Store in a sealed container in freezer or refrigerator.

Deviled Eggs

6 hard-boiled eggs, halved lengthwise
paprika to taste
2 teaspoons dry mustard
2 tablespoons plain yogurt
salt, pepper and paprika to taste

Separate yolks from egg whites. Mash yolks together in a small bowl. Add remaining ingredients, mixing well. Refill egg whites with yolk mixture. Arrange a platter and sprinkle with additional paprika.

Makes 12.

Stuffed Celery

Stuffed celery makes a great appetizer, or an easy snack for the kids.

1 bunch celery
one 8-ounce package of cream cheese
¼ cup chopped walnuts
20 small green olives, in water
2 tablespoons sour cream

Coarsely chop the olives. Separate and wash celery stalks. Cut stalks into bite size pieces. Mix the cream cheese and sour cream together. Stir in the walnuts and chopped olives. Spread filling onto the celery pieces.

Makes 10 servings.

Simply Pistou Zucchini Purée

This simple dish is delicious served with chicken or fish.

1 ½ pounds small zucchini
3 tablespoons extra-virgin olive oil
3 large cloves garlic, minced
½ cup fresh basil leaves
salt and fresh-ground pepper to taste
pinch of cayenne pepper

Cook zucchini whole in a saucepan of boiling, salted water about 10 minutes, or until they are tender enough to be easily puréed. Cut zucchini into inch pieces and place in a colander or large strainer. Press them lightly with spoon. Let stand to drain further, for 15 minutes.

Heat 2 tablespoons oil in a medium skillet, add garlic, and sauté over low heat, stirring 30 seconds. Add zucchini and cook over medium heat, stirring often, 5 minutes. Allow to cool slightly. Combine zucchini mixture and basil in a food processor and process until puréed. Keeping the processor running, gradually add remaining olive oil.

Reheat purée gently in saucepan. If it is too thin, cook over medium heat, stirring until thickened. Season with salt, pepper and cayenne pepper. Serve hot.

Makes 4 servings.

Tomato, Herb & Almond Pesto

This pesto is nice served over medleys of steamed vegetables. Take care to mix well when you do so, to stir-in the pesto's flavor.

½ cup almonds
2 cloves garlic, chopped
½ cup lightly packed basil leaves
½ cup lightly packed parsley
1 cup chopped drained tomatoes
½ teaspoon salt
1 tablespoon olive oil

Grind the almonds in a food processor. Add the garlic, basil, parsley, tomato and salt. Process until the garlic and herbs are finely minced and the ingredients are evenly blended. Add the olive oil and process until incorporated. Replace the basil with cilantro for an interesting taste variation.

Makes 4 servings (1¼ cups).

Pico de Gallo

Pico de Gallo is a no-cook salsa that goes well with almost everything, including a plate of scrambled eggs. Its flavors are best brought out by using only the freshest of ingredients.

2 to 3 fresh ripe tomatoes, diced
½ large white onion, diced
3 fresh medium-sized jalapeños, seeded and diced
1 tablespoon cilantro, chopped
salt to taste

Combine all ingredients. *Makes 2 cups.*

Herb Salsa

2 medium jalapeño peppers
2 large cloves garlic, peeled
¼ cup sprigs fresh cilantro
¼ cup sprigs fresh Italian parsley
1 pound ripe tomatoes, finely diced
¼ cup minced onion
1 to 2 tablespoons strained fresh lemon juice
1 tablespoon olive oil (optional)
1 teaspoon ground cumin
salt and freshly ground pepper to taste
1 to 2 tablespoons water, if needed

Core jalapeño peppers and remove seeds and ribs if you want them to be less spicy. Spoon jalapeño peppers and garlic into food processor and chop finely. Add cilantro and parsley and chop finely, once more. Transfer mixture to a medium-sized bowl and add tomatoes, onion, lemon juice, olive oil (if using) and cumin. Season with salt and pepper and add water if salsa is too thick. Refrigerate salsa in a covered container until ready to serve.

Makes 2½ cups.

Green Salsa

1 large onion, chopped
1 tablespoon olive oil
2 pounds fresh tomatillos or 4 10-ounce cans, drained
3 large green or poblano chiles, chopped
2 cloves garlic, minced
6 to 8 fresh jalapeños or serranos

Sauté the onion until clear; do not brown. Add the remaining ingredients and simmer for 20-30 minutes.
Makes 4 cups.

Texas Mayonnaise

1 egg
½ teaspoon dry mustard
3 tablespoons fresh lemon juice
fresh parsley, basil and oregano leaves (optional)
½ teaspoon salt
½ teaspoon ground red pepper
1 cup olive oil

In a blender or food processor, place the egg, mustard, lemon juice, salt and pepper, plus the herbs if desired. Blend for one minute. With blender or processor still running, slowly add oil until mayonnaise thickens. Add more salt or pepper to taste. Add more lemon juice, if you prefer a sharper flavor and/or a thinner consistency.

Makes 1 1/3 cups.

Eggplant Dip

This delicious treat works well served with raw vegetables, or in a small bowl as a salad.

1 firm, medium-sized eggplant
1 medium green bell pepper
1 large garlic clove
1 cup water
1 large ripe tomato, peeled and finely chopped
1 tablespoon olive oil
1 teaspoon lemon or lime juice
salt and fresh-ground pepper to taste

Preheat oven to 375 degrees. Pierce eggplant and bell pepper several times with a fork. Place in a shallow baking dish with the garlic. Add water to dish and bake vegetables until soft all over and quite deflated, about 1½ hours.

Remove from oven, cooling slightly, and then peel both eggplant and pepper, discarding seeds from pepper. Mash both vegetables (with the garlic) in a mixing bowl. Add tomato, oil, lemon or lime juice, and salt and pepper to taste. Mix well, mashing any large pieces of vegetables that might remain. Cover and chill for several hours.

Makes 6-8 servings.

Roasted Onion Dip

Make this a day in advance to allow its ingredients to blend properly.

2 large sweet onions, peeled and quartered
1 tablespoon olive oil
1 teaspoon salt
1 whole garlic head
1/3 cup sour cream
¼ cup chopped fresh parsley
1 tablespoon fresh lemon juice

Preheat oven to 425 degrees. In a large bowl, drizzle onion with oil, sprinkle with ½ teaspoon salt and toss to coat. Remove white, paper-like skin from garlic head, separate or peel the cloves and wrap them in foil. Place onion and garlic on a baking sheet and bake at 425 degrees for 1 hour. Cool 10 minutes.

Chop onion and separate the garlic cloves, squeezing to extract garlic pulp. Discard the skins. Combine onion, garlic, ½ teaspoon salt, sour cream and remaining ingredients in a large bowl. Cover and chill for 1 hour. *Makes 8 servings (¼ cup).*

Almond Butter

3 cups almonds, ground
1/3 cup olive oil

For a flour-like texture, grind the nuts more finely. Do the reverse for a more crunchy spread.

Variation: For "Cashew-almond butter," use 1½ pounds of each nut.

Cashew Butter

3 cups puréed cashews
1/3 cup extra virgin olive oil (cold pressed is always best)

Combine, spoon into jar and refrigerate.

Garlic-spiced Cheese Spread

two 8-ounce packages of cream cheese, softened
one 8-ounce package of feta cheese, crumbled
3 cloves garlic, peeled and minced
2 tablespoons chopped fresh dill

In a medium bowl, thoroughly blend cream cheese, feta cheese, garlic, and dill with an electric mixer. Cover and refrigerate for at least 4 hours. Serve with raw veggies, such as carrot sticks.

Makes 3 cups.

Guacamole

2 avocados
1 small onion, finely chopped
1 clove garlic, minced
1 ripe tomato, chopped
1 lime, juiced
salt and pepper to taste

Peel and mash avocados in a medium serving bowl. Stir in onion, garlic, tomato, lime juice, salt and pepper. Season with remaining lime juice and salt and pepper to taste. Chill for 30 minutes to an hour to blend flavors.

Homemade Barbeque Sauce

2 tablespoons butter, melted
2 tablespoons chopped onion
1 tablespoon chopped green bell pepper
1 cup water
1 cup tomato juice (or may substitute V8)
2 teaspoon mustard powder
1 teaspoon salt
1 teaspoon celery seed
2 tablespoons honey (or substitute Stevia to taste)
2 teaspoons lemon juice

Combine all ingredients. Mix well and use your choice of meat. Refrigerate leftover sauce.

Basic Hollandaise Sauce

3 egg yolks
1 tablespoon heavy cream
1 cup melted butter, cooled to room temperature
1 tablespoon lemon juice
½ teaspoon salt
dash of cayenne pepper

Use a double boiler. Off the heat, put the egg yolks and cream in the upper section of the double boiler and stir with a wire whisk vigorously until well blended. Place the container over hot water. Stirring the eggs continuously, bring the water slowly to a simmer. *Do not let it boil.*

Stir, taking care that no film forms at the bottom. When the eggs have thickened to the consistency of heavy cream, slowly add the cooled melted butter, stirring vigorously. Add the lemon juice a drop at a time, while continuing to stir. Immediately remove from heat. Add the salt and cayenne.

Creamy Herb Dressing

Jami's Favorite

¼ small bunch of dill, stems removed (about ¼ cup of loosely packed leaves)

¼ bunch of flat-leaf parsley, stems removed (about ¾ cup of loosely packed leaves)

¼ bunch of thyme, stems removed (about 2 tablespoons of loosely packed leaves)

½ bunch of chives, coarsely chopped (1/3 cup)

¾ cup Texas Mayonnaise

½ cup plain yogurt

1 tablespoon apple cider vinegar

½ teaspoon salt; more to taste

1/8 teaspoon pepper

¾ teaspoon tomato juice

¼ teaspoon jalapeño pepper, minced

In a food processor, chop dill, parsley, thyme and chives with mayonnaise. With the motor still running, slowly pour in yogurt. Follow with apple cider vinegar, salt, pepper, tomato juice and minced jalapeño pepper. Adjust seasoning to taste. Pour into a bottle or jar and refrigerate for up to 2 weeks. *Great for both salads and as a marinade.*

Herb Butter

1 lb butter, cut into pieces and softened at room temperature
¼ cup lemon juice
4 cups assorted fresh tender herb leaves (choose from tarragon, thyme, parsley, basil, dill, chives, marjoram, chervil)
salt and pepper to taste

In a food processor, combine the butter, salt and pepper. Process until you get a creamy paste, scraping down the sides as necessary, and then add the lemon juice and process until creamy. Add the herb leaves and process again until well blended. Shape into 2 logs in parchment or waxed paper, roll tightly, wrap well in plastic and chill. Can be frozen for up to 2 months. Cut off a slice and lay it on the hot food just before serving. *Great with salmon!*

Zesty Salsa Dip

6 tomatoes, diced
½ cup diced yellow onion
1 jalapeño, seeded and diced
2 cloves garlic, peeled and minced
2 tablespoons chopped fresh parsley
1 tablespoon minced fresh cilantro
1 teaspoon crushed oregano
2 tablespoons olive oil
½ tablespoon apple cider vinegar
¼ teaspoon salt
1/8 teaspoon ground black pepper

Combine ingredients in a large bowl and mix well. Serve with vegetable slices or your favorite dish.

Etoufee Sauce

1 teaspoon olive oil
1 large onion, cut into strips
1 large green bell pepper, cut into strips
1 teaspoon garlic, minced
¼ pound smoked sausage (andouille or kielbasa) sliced into thin, half-circles
1 cup tomatoes, diced
½ teaspoon cayenne pepper

Sauté the bell pepper, onion and garlic in olive oil until soft. Add the remaining ingredients and simmer for 25 minutes. Serve warm.

Cuban Marinade

2 teaspoons garlic powder
4 tablespoons lime juice
1 teaspoon onion powder
1 teaspoon ground cumin
½ teaspoon oregano
½ teaspoon thyme
1 teaspoon cilantro
2 teaspoon parsley
1 teaspoon salt; ° teaspoon pepper
3 tablespoons olive oil

Combine ingredients and mix well. *Great for chicken!*

Artichoke & Spinach Dip

1 cup chopped artichoke hearts
½ cup chopped spinach
8 oz. cream cheese
½ cup plain yogurt
½ teaspoon crushed red pepper flakes
¼ teaspoon salt
1/8 teaspoon garlic powder
dash of black pepper

Boil the spinach and artichoke hearts in a cup of water in a small saucepan over medium heat until tender, about 10 minutes. Drain well in a colander. Heat the cream cheese in a saucepan over medium heat until hot. Add the spinach and artichoke hearts to the cream cheese and stir well. Add the remaining ingredients and again, stir well. Serve hot with celery and carrots, or your favorite vegetable.

Almost Tartar Sauce

1 pint plain yogurt
½ cup green onions, tops included, coarsely chopped
¼ cup cucumber, finely chopped
juice of ½ to 1 freshly squeezed lemon
1 teaspoon capers
1 teaspoon sea salt; ¼ teaspoon pepper; ¼ teaspoon Mrs. Dash
¼ cup parsely, no heavy stems, coarsely chopped

Feed all ingredients except yogurt through a meat grinder using the coarse blade, or use a blender on 'chop.' Stir results into yogurt and chill. Serve with fish, or with veggie slices and chunks.

Vegetable Dishes

Vegetable Dishes

Vegetable Dishes (Continued)

People on the diet have long had to make do with simple dinners such as steamed broccoli and grilled salmon, while the rest of the family ate "real food." This section should help you solve that problem. If you have an anti-veggie spouse or children, challenge them to eat well for two weeks. I promise you, they will feel so good, they may never go back to "real food."

Red Pepper & Broccoli Sauté

Boiling the broccoli in this dish insures that it retains its bright color.

1 pound broccoli, thick stems removed
1 to 2 tablespoons olive oil
2 red bell peppers, cut into strips
2 large cloves garlic, chopped
2 tablespoons fresh Italian parsley, chopped
2 tablespoons water
salt and fresh-ground pepper to taste

Divide broccoli into medium-sized florets. Add to sauté pan of boiling salted water and boil uncovered for 3 minutes. Use a colander or strainer to drain, rinse broccoli under cold water, and then drain well once more.

Heat oil in the same pan. Add peppers and sauté over medium heat for 3 minutes. Cover and cook over low heat, stirring often, for about 5 minutes or until nearly tender. Add garlic and parsley and sauté, stirring constantly, for about 15 seconds. Spoon in broccoli and 2 tablespoons water. Sprinkle vegetables with salt and pepper, cover and cook over medium-low heat, stirring often for about 2 minutes or until broccoli is crisp-tender. Serve hot.

Makes 3-4 servings.

Leek Compote

Leek compote is a delicious and simple delicacy. The leeks are cooked until tender with only delicate seasoning, leaving the flavor of the vegetable intact. Leeks go well with chicken and fish. For this dish, use the white and light-to-medium-green parts of the leeks; the dark-green parts are best frozen for use later, in soups and stocks.

2 pounds leeks, rinsed, halved and thinly sliced
2 to 3 tablespoons oil or butter
salt and fresh-ground pepper to taste
1 ½ teaspoons fresh thyme (dried ¼ teaspoon)
¼ cup chicken or vegetable stock

Spoon sliced leeks into a bowl of cold water, separating them into pieces. Allow to seep 5 minutes and remove to a colander to drain. If water becomes sandy, soak and drain leeks again.

Heat oil in a heavy casserole or stew pan. Add leeks, salt and pepper. Cover and cook over low heat, stirring occasionally, for 5 minutes. Add thyme and stock, cover and cook, stirring occasionally once again, for about 15 minutes or until leeks are tender. If mixture remains soupy, uncover and cook, stirring often, to evaporate the excess liquid. Adjust seasoning and serve hot.

Makes 4-6 servings.

Braised Butternut Squash

with ginger and onions

You can cut down on the braising time required for this dish by simply microwaving the squash. This not only shortens the cooking time, but it also saves the trouble of cutting the skins off the squash. A microwave is especially useful if you want to substitute one of the ridged squashes such as sweet dumpling or acorn, which would be very difficult to braise. Simply scoop out the cooked pulp and braise it briefly with the recipe's herbs and spices.

2½ pounds butternut squash
1 to 2 tablespoons olive oil
1 medium-sized onion, minced
1 tablespoon minced peeled fresh ginger
¼ cup vegetable broth or water
½ teaspoon ground ginger
salt and fresh-ground pepper to taste

Halve squash and remove seeds and strings. Place cut-side down in a microwave-safe baking dish, add 2 tablespoons water and cover with wax paper. Microwave on high for about 15 minutes or until tender — check by piercing squash at its thickest part with a fork. Remove squash pulp from peel and roughly dice.

Heat oil in a large skillet or sauté pan. Add onion and sauté over medium heat, stirring often, for 7 minutes. Spoon in minced ginger and sauté over low heat for 30 seconds. Add squash pieces, ¼ cup broth, ground ginger, salt and pepper. Cover and cook, stirring often, for about 5 minutes or until squash is both coated with herbs and spices and is heated through. Squash pieces may fall apart in the process. Serve hot.

Makes 4 servings.

Roasted Bell Peppers

To roast bell peppers, place them directly on a gas burner or on a baking sheet about 7-8 inches from the broiler. Roast, turning occasionally, until peppers are blackened and charred on all sides. Wrap peppers in a damp paper towels and place in a plastic bag. Seal bag and allow peppers to steam within for 10-15 minutes. Remove black charred outside skin from peppers with a sharp paring knife. Finally, use a paring knife to remove seeds and stems. Peppers can be placed in a jar or bowl, covered with olive oil and then refrigerated, covered, for up to 3 days. Drain and pat dry before using.

Parsley-spiced Baby Carrots

1 ½ cup baby carrots
¼ cup water
pinch salt
2 teaspoons butter
1 ½ teaspoon finely chopped fresh parsley

Place the carrots, water and salt in small skillet and bring to a boil over medium-high heat. Reduce heat to medium, cover, and cook for 5 minutes or just until tender. Add a little more water during cooking if the skillet becomes too dry, but only enough to prevent scorching.

Add butter to skillet and raise heat to medium-high. Cook, stirring frequently, for another minute or two, or until most of the liquid evaporates. Toss in parsley and serve hot.

Makes 2 servings.

Dill-spiced Baby Carrots

6 cups baby carrots (about 1 ½ pounds)
¾ cup water
1/8 teaspoon salt
3 tablespoons butter
1 tablespoon finely chopped fresh dill (dried 1 teaspoon)

Place the carrots, water and salt in large, nonstick skillet and bring to a boil over medium-high heat. Reduce the heat to medium, cover, and cook for 5-7 minutes, or just until the carrots are tender. Add a little more water during cooking if the skillet becomes too dry, but only enough to prevent scorching.

Add the butter to the skillet, and raise the heat to medium-high. Cook, stirring frequently, for another minute or two, or until most of the liquid evaporates. Toss in dill and serve hot.

Makes 8 servings.

Sautéed Onions and Squash

2 tablespoons butter
3½ cups sliced zucchini squash (about 1 pound)
3½ cups sliced yellow squash (about 1 pound)
1 medium-sized yellow onion
¾ teaspoon dried savory, dill, or parsley
½ teaspoon salt
¼ teaspoon ground black pepper

Place the butter in a large, deep skillet and place over medium-high heat. Cut onion into ¼ inch thick slices, separate into rings and add to skillet. Spoon in remaining ingredients and cook, stirring a couple of times, for 3 minutes.

Reduce heat to medium and cook, stirring occasionally, for an additional 5 minutes, or until the squash is crisp-tender. Serve hot.

Makes 8 servings.

Stuffed Zucchini

This dish features zucchini lightly stuffed with a pungent combination of parsley, garlic and olive oil.

8 small zucchini, about 4 inches long
5 plump garlic cloves, smashed and minced
2/3 cup fresh flat-leaf parsley, minced
½ cup extra-virgin olive oil
salt and fresh-ground black pepper

Preheat oven to 450 degrees. With a sharp knife, make a long, ½ inch deep and slightly angled slice along the tops of each zucchini. To create a shallow cavity in each zucchini, make a second, slightly angled slice ¾ inch from the first cut and remove wedge.

In a small bowl, blend together garlic, parsley, half of the olive oil, salt and pepper. Stuff mixture into zucchini cavities, packing tightly. Arrange zucchinis in a shallow baking dish just large enough to hold them. Drizzle with remaining ¼ cup olive oil.

Bake until zucchini are tender and stuffing is brown on top, or 15-20 minutes.

Makes 4 servings.

Curried Cauliflower

1 to 2 cups cauliflower, cut into bite-sized pieces
1 onion, thinly sliced
½ cup chicken stock
½ teaspoon butter
1 teaspoon curry powder (or to taste)
½ teaspoon cumin (optional)

Combine ingredients in a small pan and cover. Simmer until most of the liquid has evaporated.

Makes 2 servings.

Carrots with Caraway

6 carrots, sliced (about 3 cups)
1 teaspoon olive oil
2 teaspoons caraway seeds

Place sliced carrots in a small saucepan and cover with water. Gently simmer until carrots soften. Drain and add oil, mixing until carrots are covered. Stir in caraway seeds.

Makes 6 servings.

Pepper-Okra Sauté

2 teaspoons butter
1 cup yellow bell pepper strips
1 cup red bell pepper strips
3 cups okra pods (about ½ pound), cut in half diagonally
2 tablespoons chopped fresh cilantro
¼ teaspoon each of salt and black pepper

Heat butter in a large pan over medium heat. Add bell peppers and sauté for 4 minutes. Stir in okra, cover, reduce heat and cook for 15 minutes or until okra is tender. Mix in seasonings.

Makes 4 servings.

Italian Vegetable Medley

1 clove garlic, minced
1 onion, sliced
2 teaspoons olive oil
3 cups combined red, yellow or green bell peppers, sliced
2 zucchini, sliced (about 2 cups)
salt to taste
1 teaspoon thyme, oregano or basil, or a combination of all

In a large skillet, sauté garlic and onion in olive oil. Add a splash of water and cook vegetables until tender. Stir in pepper, zucchini, salt and herbs. Cover and cook until tender.

Makes 8 servings.

Sautéed Leek

1 leek, cleaned thoroughly and bulb sliced
1 teaspoon olive oil
2 cups sliced carrots
¼ teaspoon thyme

In a small saucepan, sauté leek in olive oil. Add a splash of water and cook until tender. Add carrots and thyme. Cover and cook over low heat until carrots are tender.

Makes 4 servings.

Curried Zucchini

1 clove garlic, minced
½ cup chopped onion
1 teaspoon olive oil
½ teaspoon salt
½ to 1 teaspoon turmeric
¼ to ½ teaspoon cumin
½ teaspoon red pepper flakes (optional)
3 zucchini, sliced (about 3 cups)
2 tomatoes, chopped

In a large skillet, sauté garlic and onion in olive oil until they soften. Add salt, turmeric, cumin and red peppers. Blend well, stir in zucchini and cook until tender. Stir in tomatoes and serve. *Makes 8 servings.*

Creamed Spinach

1 pound fresh spinach
1 medium onion, chopped
1 clove garlic, crushed
¼ cup butter, melted
½ cup of sour cream
pinch of salt
¼ teaspoon pepper
pinch of ground nutmeg
paprika

Remove stems, wash spinach leaves thoroughly and tear into large pieces. Cook in a small amount of boiling water 5 to 8 minutes or until tender. Drain, lay out on paper towels and blot until barely moist.

Sauté onion and garlic in butter in a large skillet until tender. Stir in sour cream and next 3 ingredients. Add spinach and cook over low heat until thoroughly heated. Sprinkle with paprika and serve.

Makes 4 servings.

Caramelized Onions

4 medium-sized onions (2 pounds)
1 tablespoon chopped fresh parsley
1 tablespoon chopped fresh chives
1 tablespoon chopped fresh thyme
1 teaspoon salt
½ teaspoon pepper
1 tablespoon butter
1 tablespoon olive oil

Cut onions into ¼-inch thick slices and separate into rings. In a large bowl, combine onion rings, parsley and next 4 ingredients, tossing to coat.

Melt butter in a large heavy skillet or Dutch oven over medium heat. Add oil and onion mixture and cook 25 minutes or until onion is browned and tender, stirring often.

Makes 5 servings.

Stir-fried Zucchini

If you should be interrupted mid-preparation, don't worry; the longer the zucchini sits in the salt, the better this recipe will taste. For a colorful twist, substitute green, red and white peppercorns for the black pepper.

12 ounces zucchini (about 2 zucchinis)
2 teaspoons coarse salt
olive oil
fresh-ground black pepper to taste

Trim and cut zucchini into thin rounds. Transfer to a colander, salt and let sit for at least 15 minutes. Preheat a medium skillet over high heat. Pat the zucchini rounds dry with paper towels, and then rub olive oil on each round. Spoon into preheated skillet and stir frequently for about 2 minutes, until the zucchini begins to brown. Season to taste with black pepper.

Makes 4 servings.

Stir-fried Vegetable Medley

with eggplant and tomato

2 cloves garlic
1 onion, sliced
2 teaspoons olive oil
3 cups of sliced red, green and yellow bell peppers
2 zucchini, sliced (about 3 cups)
4 tomatoes, or one 28 oz. can of Italian plum tomatoes, drained
salt to taste
1 bay leaf
1 teaspoon dried basil (fresh 2 tablespoons, chopped)
1 small eggplant, cubed and steamed (about 2 cups)

Cut tomatoes into cubes. Sauté garlic and onion in olive oil in a medium-large casserole dish. Add peppers, zucchini, tomatoes, salt, bay leaf and basil. Cover and simmer until vegetables are tender (about 15-20 minutes). Add steamed eggplant and cook for 5 more minutes.

Makes 10 servings.

Buttered, Lemony Asparagus

1 pound fresh asparagus spears
3 tablespoons butter
1 tablespoon lemon juice
½ teaspoon grated lemon peel

Snap off tough ends of asparagus. In large skillet, combine asparagus spears and ½ cup water. Bring to a boil over medium heat. Cook 5-10 minutes or until crisp-tender. Drain.

Melt butter in a small saucepan. Stir in lemon juice and lemon peel. Place asparagus on serving platter and top with butter mixture.

Makes 4 servings.

Stir-Fried Cabbage

2 tablespoons vegetable oil
1 teaspoon sesame oil
1 garlic clove, minced
1 teaspoon grated ginger root
1 cup shredded cabbage
1 cup shredded Chinese cabbage
1 cup shredded bok choy
½ cup chopped green onions
2 teaspoons sesame seeds, toasted if desired

In a large skillet or wok, combine oils and heat over high heat. Add garlic and ginger root and cook a few seconds. Fold in cabbage, Chinese cabbage, bok choy and onions, mixing well. Cook 2-3 minutes or until cabbage is crisp-tender, stirring constantly. Place in serving bowl and sprinkle with sesame seeds.

Makes 4 servings.

Zucchini in Tomato Sauce

1 medium-sized onion, finely chopped
2 tablespoon olive oil
1 clove garlic, minced or pressed
3 medium-sized tomatoes, peeled and chopped
½ teaspoon each salt and dried basil leaves
¼ teaspoon dried oregano leaves
dash pepper
¼ cup chicken broth
1½ pounds zucchini (4 to 6 medium-sized), sliced ¼ inch thick

Cook onion in oil in a large frying pan until soft but not browned. Mix in garlic, tomatoes, salt, basil, oregano, pepper and broth. Bring to a boil and cover. Reduce heat and simmer for 20 minutes.

Uncover, mixing in zucchini. Cook over moderately high heat, stirring frequently, until tomato sauce thickens and zucchini is tender-crisp (about 10 minutes). Add salt to taste.

Makes 4 servings.

Baked Cabbage

1 large head of green cabbage
4 small red tomatoes, diced
1 small, white onion, chopped
½ teaspoon garlic powder
½ teaspoon salt
1 teaspoon black pepper
1/8 teaspoon cumin
1/8 teaspoon caraway seed
1/8 cup water or chicken broth

Preheat oven to 325 degrees. Quarter the cabbage and boil it in a large pot for 10 minutes. Remove cabbage sections and place them in a shallow baking dish. Combine other ingredients in a small bowl and pour over cabbage. Bake for 30 minutes, or until liquid is absorbed. Turn cabbage pieces halfway through cooking time to prevent top side from overcooking.

Makes 4 servings.

Spinach Casserole

2 packages of frozen, chopped spinach (10 ounces each)
2 teaspoons instant minced onion
1 clove garlic, minced
1 teaspoon salt
1/8 teaspoon pepper
2/3 cup sour cream
2 tablespoons goat's milk
2 tablespoons butter, softened

Preheat oven to 325 degrees. Thaw spinach, squeezing to drain it thoroughly. Combine all ingredients in a bowl and spoon into an ungreased, 1-quart casserole. Cover and bake 40-50 minutes.

Makes 6 servings.

Rutabagas & Mixed Veggies

8 tablespoons butter
1 large, yellow onion cut into wedges
1 (about ½ lb) rutabaga, peeled and cut into ½ inch slices
1 pound carrots, peeled and sliced
1 red bell pepper cut into thin strips
salt and pepper to taste

Melt butter in a large, heavy skillet over medium heat. Add vegetables, stirring to coat. Reduce heat to medium-low and cook 30 minutes or until vegetables are tender, stirring occasionally.

Makes 8 servings.

Baked Parsnips & Rutabaga

1 pound parsnips, peeled and chopped into ½ half inch pieces
1 ¼ pounds rutabaga, peeled and chopped into ½ inch pieces
1 small onion, chopped
4 large cloves garlic, finely chopped
2 teaspoons dried oregano
salt and pepper to taste
3 teaspoons olive oil
½ cup water

Preheat oven to 400 degrees. In a baking dish, toss all of the ingredients (except the water) until well combined. Pour in the water. Cover tightly and bake until just tender, or about 40 minutes. Uncover and bake until lightly browned, or about 20 minutes.

Makes 4 servings.

Sautéed Carrots & Asparagus

2 pounds asparagus
3 large carrots
¼ cup olive oil
peeled garlic cloves (whole or cut)
1 can diced tomatoes

Pour oil into fry pan over medium heat. Add cleaned asparagus, cut off at tips. Clean carrots, cut them off at the tips, peel and then slice them into long strips to match the asparagus. Add carrots and garlic cloves to asparagus in fry pan and cook 15 minutes, stirring frequently. Add diced tomatoes and simmer for 10 minutes. Season with salt and pepper to taste.

Creamy Brussels & Pecans

1 ½ pounds small Brussels sprouts, trimmed
¼ cup whipping cream
5 large garlic cloves, chopped
3/4 cup pecans, toasted
3/4 cup packed fresh basil leaves
1 ½ teaspoons grated lemon peel
fresh basil sprigs (optional)
lemon wedges (optional)

Combine Brussels sprouts, cream and garlic in a heavy, large skillet. Bring to a boil over medium-low heat. Cover skillet tightly and cook until Brussels sprouts are crisp-tender but still bright green, and almost all cream is absorbed (about 10 minutes).

Use a processor to finely grind pecans, basil leaves and lemon peel. Add to sprouts mixture in skillet and toss until sprouts are coated. Season with salt and pepper and transfer to serving bowel. Garnish with basil sprigs and lemon wedges, if desired, and serve.

Makes 6-8 servings.

Italian Brussels Sprouts

2 tablespoons butter
2 tablespoons fresh garlic, chopped
1 yellow onion, finely diced
2 pounds Brussels sprouts (large ones halved)
1 pound diced tomatoes (seeds discarded)
2 tablespoons fresh basil
2 cups heavy whipping cream
1 tablespoon salt
1 tablespoon fresh-ground black pepper

Melt butter in a pan and sauté garlic and onions until golden. Add Brussels sprouts and tomatoes and sauté for about 5 minutes. Add basil, heavy cream, salt and pepper and cook until sprouts turn tender.

Brussels Sprouts & Chestnuts

1½ pounds chestnuts
1 pound trimmed Brussels sprouts
1 ounce butter

Preheat oven to 400 degrees. With the point of a sharp knife, make a small cut on the flat side of each chestnut. Bake the nuts in their skins for 20 minutes, then peel off the outer shell and the inner skin. Nuts are easier to peel while still hot.

Boil Brussels sprouts 8-10 minutes, or until just tender. Drain. Over high heat, toss the chestnuts and Brussels sprouts with butter, until the butter is completely melted. Serve immediately.

Buttered Broccoli

3 cups broccoli
1 tablespoon butter
sea salt to taste

Place broccoli in a small saucepan and cover with water. Bring water to a boil at high heat. Reduce to medium heat and continue cooking until tender, about 10-15 minutes. Drain water and add butter, mixing until broccoli is covered. Add sea salt to taste.

Shredded Brussels Sprouts

1 ½ pounds Brussels sprouts
4 tablespoons unsalted, real butter
½ teaspoon salt
¼ teaspoon white pepper
2 teaspoons water
Juice of ½ lime

To clean them, soak whole sprouts in a large bowl of cold salt water. Trim and discard ends and any bitter leaves. Cut each in half lengthwise, then slice thinly across width. Melt butter in large skillet over medium high heat. Sauté sprouts with salt and pepper until they start to brown. Add water and cook until barely limp, or about 4 minutes. Stir in lime juice and serve immediately. *Makes 6-8 servings.*

Brussels Sprouts Medley

1 pound Brussels sprouts
boiling salt water
1 sweet red bell pepper, seeded, thinly sliced
1 medium onion, slivered
3 tablespoons butter
1 clove garlic, minced or pressed
salt to taste

Trim stem ends and any discolored leaves from Brussels sprouts. Cut an "X" into stem end of each. Cook in about 1 inch boiling salted water, uncovered for 4-5 minutes, then longer (or, if you prefer steam, covered, over boiling water until just tender, 8-10 minutes). Meanwhile cook red pepper and onion in butter in a medium frying pan over moderate heat, stirring frequently, until onions are tender and lightly browned. Mix in garlic and cook 30 seconds longer.

Drain Brussels sprouts well. Combine lightly with red pepper mixture. Taste. Add salt if needed.

Makes 4 servings.

Cauliflower Delight

Before cooking, you might wish to soak the cauliflower head in salted, cold water for a few minutes, to remove any impurities.

1 large head cauliflower, about 2 pounds
4 to 6 slices of uncured bacon
1 green pepper, seeded
3 tablespoons chopped parsley
salt

Wash and trim cauliflower and remove most of the outer leaves. Put whole head in a pot filled with 2-3 inches of boiling salted water. Cover. Steam cauliflower about 15 minutes or until tender crisp, not overcooked.

Cut the turkey bacon and green pepper into strips. Sauté turkey bacon until soft or crisp to your liking. Drain and keep warm. Sauté pepper in same pan with bacon drippings. Place cooked cauliflower on a serving dish. Top with bacon-pepper mixture. Sprinkle with parsley.

Makes 4 servings.

Curried Cauliflower

Cauliflower releases enough liquid to steam itself.

2 teaspoons olive oil
2 cups thinly sliced onions
2 tablespoons finely chopped peeled fresh ginger
2 tablespoons curry powder mixture (opposite page)
1 tablespoon minced garlic
10 cups cauliflower florets (2 medium-sized heads)
1 cup chopped, seeded and peeled tomato
1 cup plain yogurt
½ cup finely chopped cilantro stems
1 teaspoon salt
8 lemon wedges (optional)
cilantro sprigs (optional)

Heat the oil in a Dutch oven over medium-high heat. Add onion and ginger; cover and cook 3 minutes, stirring frequently. Reduce heat to medium. Add curry powder mixture and garlic, cook 30 seconds, stirring constantly. Add cauliflower and next 4 ingredients (cauliflower through salt), stirring well to combine. Bring to a boil (yogurt will curdle); cover, reduce heat, and simmer 20 minutes or until cauliflower is tender. Serve with lemon wedges and cilantro sprigs, if desired.

Makes 8 servings.

Curry Powder

3 tablespoons paprika
2 teaspoons ground cumin
1 teaspoon ground ginger
1 teaspoon ground turmeric
1 teaspoon ground coriander
½ teaspoon cardamom
½ teaspoon ground red pepper

Combine all ingredients. *Makes 1/3 cup.*

Mashed Rutabaga

This Midwestern dish is great with turkey or chicken.

4 rutabagas
4 carrots
2 tablespoons powdered Stevia
2 tablespoons butter
1/8 cup goat's milk

Peel rutabagas and cut into large cubes. Place in cold, salted water and bring to a boil. Reduce heat and cook at medium-high until fork tender. Drain and mash rutabagas together with grated carrots, Stevia and butter. Spoon into a casserole dish, cover and place in oven on low to keep warm. If dish dries, stir in a little milk.

Makes 10 servings.

Spinach and Brussels Sprouts

1 pound Brussels, washed and cleaned
1 pound spinach, washed and cleaned
3 tablespoons butter
salt and pepper

Boil sprouts in salted water for 25 minutes, then drain. Do the same for the spinach, for 2 minutes, then drain. Combine vegetables, butter, salt and pepper in a baking dish. Bake at 350 degrees for six minutes. Serve hot.

Cauliflower with Herb Butter

1 large cauliflower
juice of 1 lemon
1/3 cup butter, melted
1 tablespoon chopped fresh parsley
1 tablespoon chopped fresh basil (¼ teaspoon dried basil)
¼ teaspoon salt
1 clove garlic, crushed
lemon twists and fresh parsley sprigs (optional garnish)

Remove cauliflower's large outer leaves and break it into florets. Cover and cook in a small amount of boiling water 8 to 10 minutes or until tender. Drain, arrange on a serving dish and sprinkle with lemon juice.

Combine melted butter with the next 4 ingredients and pour over florets. Garnish if desired.

Makes 6 servings.

Hollandaise Broccoli

3 cups broccoli
1 tablespoon grape seed or olive oil

Place broccoli in a small saucepan and cover with water. Add oil. Bring water to a boil at high heat. Reduce to medium heat and continue cooking until tender, about 10-15 minutes. Drain water, cover with "Basic Hollandaise Sauce" and serve.

Best Broccoli

1 ½ pound fresh broccoli
10 large cloves fresh garlic unpeeled
1/3 cup apple cider vinegar
3 tablespoons olive oil
2 teaspoons salt

Separate broccoli into florets with stems. Crush garlic. Fill large pot with water and add all ingredients. Cook, covered, until broccoli is tender. Drain and refrigerate overnight.

Broccoli Rabe

1 pound broccoli rabe, trimmed
5 tablespoons olive oil
1 clove garlic, minced

Bring a large pot of salted water to a boil. Cut an X in the bottom of the stems of broccoli rabe and place in the boiling water. Cook until tender but still firm, about 5 minutes. Drain. In a large skillet over medium heat, heat olive oil and sauté garlic for 1 to 2 minutes. Stir in the broccoli rabe and sauté 10 to 15 minutes.

Lemon-Almond Broccoli

1 head fresh broccoli, cut into florets
1/4 cup butter, melted
2 tablespoons lemon juice
1/4 cup blanched almonds

Steam or boil broccoli until tender. Drain. In a small saucepan, melt butter over medium heat. Remove from heat. Stir in lemon juice and almonds. Pour over hot broccoli and serve.

Broccoli with Bacon

2 pounds fresh broccoli
6 slices bacon
3/4 cup coarsely chopped walnuts (optional)
1/2 cup sliced green onions

Remove broccoli leaves, cut tough stalk ends off. Wash spears. Cook in boiling water for 6 to 8 minutes or until tender. In a separate pan, cook bacon until brown. Remove from heat and crumble. Cook walnuts, if desired in bacon drippings over medium heat, stirring constantly (about 3 minutes). Add green onions, and cook for 2 minutes, stirring constantly. Transfer broccoli to serving dish. Spoon walnut/onion mixture over broccoli. Sprinkle bacon on.

Broccoli in Herbed Butter

1 pound fresh broccoli, cut into spears
1 ½ teaspoons onion, finely chopped
2 tablespoons butter
1 ½ teaspoons lemon juice
¼ teaspoon salt
1/8 teaspoon thyme

Steam broccoli until crisp-tender (about 5 minutes). In a separate pan, melt butter; add lemon juice, onions and herbs. Drain broccoli and place in a serving dish. Pour butter/herb mixture to coat broccoli.

Broccoli with Cashews

1 large bunch fresh broccoli
2 tablespoons onion, minced
1 cup roasted cashews
2 tablespoons butter
1 cup sour cream
½ teaspoon apple cider vinegar
¼ teaspoon salt
½ teaspoon paprika
Stevia or honey to taste (approximately 1 teaspoon)

Preheat oven to 325 degrees. Cook broccoli in water until crisp. Sauté onion in butter. Stir in sour cream and remaining ingredients, except cashews. Layer broccoli in a buttered 1½ quart baking dish and cover with sauce. Sprinkle with cashews and bake uncovered for 25 minutes.

Lemon-garlic Broccoli

2 pounds ready-cut broccoli florets
1 clove garlic, minced
3 tablespoons olive oil
3 tablespoons lemon juice
salt to taste

Steam broccoli until tender but firm, 4-6 minutes. Meanwhile, mince the garlic. Heat the oil in a nonstick pan over medium heat; add the garlic and sauté for 1 minute. Add the cooked broccoli, lemon juice, and salt to taste. Cook briefly, just to combine all ingredients.

Roast Pepper & Nut Broccoli

5 cups broccoli florets; bite-size
2 large red bell peppers, roasted, peeled and sliced
3 tablespoons pine nuts, lightly toasted
2½ tablespoons olive oil
3 tablespoons shallots, minced
½ teaspoon salt
½ teaspoon pepper

Cook florets in boiling water until barely done. Drain in a colander, refresh under cold water. In a 12 inch skillet, heat the oil over low heat. Sauté shallots, stirring constantly, until very lightly golden, about 2 minutes. Add broccoli and roasted peppers; cook until vegetables are warmed through; add salt and pepper. Transfer to platter and garnish with pine nuts.

Tomato-herbed Broccoli

1 ½ pounds broccoli, cut into inch pieces
2 plum or roma tomatoes, chopped
1 clove garlic, crushed
1 tablespoon olive oil
¼ teaspoon basil
¼ teaspoon oregano
¼ teaspoon salt

Heat 1 inch water to boiling in 3-quart saucepan; add broccoli. Cover and heat to boiling; reduce heat. Simmer until broccoli is crisp-tender; drain. Heat oil in 10-inch skillet over medium-high heat. Heat remaining ingredients in skillet 1 to 3 minutes, stirring constantly until hot. Pour over broccoli and toss.

Lemon-pepper Broccoli

4 cups small broccoli florets
2 tablespoons freshly grated lemon peel
1 tablespoon olive oil
1/8 teaspoon crushed red pepper
1/8 teaspoon salt

Bring 1 inch of water to boil in a medium saucepan. Place broccoli in saucepan, cover and cook for 2 minutes, or until broccoli is crisp-tender. Drain and let broccoli cool. Heat oil in a medium skillet over medium heat. Add lemon peel, crushed red pepper and stir until peel begins to brown, about 30 seconds. Add broccoli and salt and stir until hot, about 1 minute.

Italian Broccoli

1 large bunch broccoli
1 small onion, chopped
1 cup zucchini, shredded
8 large cloves fresh garlic, chopped
1 egg, beaten lightly
½ cup olive oil
¼ teaspoon oregano
salt and pepper to taste

Steam or boil broccoli until tender. Drain and mash, as you would potatoes, leaving small bits of broccoli. In a large skillet, sauté onion, zucchini and garlic in oil. Once the onion begins to brown, mix in broccoli. Stir in oregano, remove from heat and add egg, salt and pepper, blending well. Spoon into a casserole dish. When ready to serve, bake at 350 degrees for about 15 minutes.

Macadamia Broccoli

2 pounds broccoli
½ cup water
¼ cup macadamia nut oil
2 garlic cloves, minced
1 teaspoon salt
1/8 teaspoon pepper

Cut ends of broccoli stalks lengthwise into halves or quarters, depending on size. Place in a large skillet. Sprinkle with water, oil, garlic, salt and pepper. Cover tightly; sauté over very low heat 20 to 30 minutes. Turn broccoli several times during cooking.

Baked Basil Broccoli

4½ cups broccoli, coarsely chopped
12 cherry tomatoes, halved
½ cup water
4 egg whites
2 egg yolks
2 teaspoons lemon juice
½ teaspoon basil
¼ teaspoon salt; 1/8 teaspoon pepper
fresh basil leaves (optional)
olive oil

Combine broccoli and water in saucepan; bring to a boil. Reduce heat to medium and cook 10 minutes, or until tender. Drain and rinse with cold water.

Line a 7½ by 3 by 2 inch loaf pan with foil sized to extend 3 inches beyond the sides of the pan. Coat the foil with cool olive oil. Combine broccoli, egg white, egg yolks, lemon juice, basil, salt and pepper in processor until smooth. Spoon into prepared pan and carefully fold foil to cover.

Place loaf pan in a larger baking dish into which an inch of hot water has been poured, to a depth of 1 inch. Bake for 1 hour, or until the dish's edges are firm and the center is set.

Remove loaf and let cool on a wire rack for 15 minutes. Loosen the edges and invert on a serving platter. Smooth edges as necessary. Cut into 16 slices; arrange 2 slices on each of 8 individual plates. Garnish with cherry tomato halves and basil leaves.

Spicy Broccoli

1 bunch broccoli cut into florets
1 tablespoon olive oil
½ teaspoon red pepper flakes
1 garlic clove put through a press

In a large skillet, heat the oil over medium heat. Add the broccoli, give it a quick stir and cook it covered, stirring occasionally, for 3 minutes or until crisp. Turn the heat to low and cook it for 2 minutes until it is just tender. Add the red pepper flakes, garlic, salt and pepper to taste and cook the mixture for 1 minute.

Italian Carrots

3 tablespoon olive oil
1 pound carrots, peeled and sliced thin
2 tablespoons fresh chopped parsley
3 tablespoons butter
salt and pepper to taste

Scrape carrots and slice thin. Melt butter in oil in pan. When butter and oil are hot, add carrots and mix well. Let carrots soak on the bottom and sauté. Add parsley and mix well. Add salt and pepper to taste. Simmer until carrots are cooked but still firm.

Carrots Vinaigrette

1 pound carrots
½ cup olive oil
1/3 cup apple cider vinegar
1 tablespoon minced garlic

1 teaspoon salt
¼ teaspoon pepper

Peel carrots and cut into slices. Place carrots in a large skillet. Add water to cover. Cover skillet and heat to boiling. Boiling until carrots are crisp tender, about 3 minutes. Meanwhile, whisk remaining ingredients in a small bowl until smooth. Drain carrots, toss with vinaigrette and serve.

Fried Shredded Carrots

4 carrots, shredded
2 tablespoons olive oil
½ tablespoon minced garlic
salt and pepper to taste

Heat oil in skillet over medium heat. Sauté garlic for 1 minute. Stir in carrots and fry for a few minutes, until carrots are tender. Add salt and pepper to taste, and serve.

Honey Glazed Carrots

1 pound baby carrots
2 tablespoons butter
2 tablespoons honey
1 tablespoon lemon juice

Submerge carrots in water and boil until tender. Melt butter in a skillet; stir in honey and lemon juice. Heat for 5 minutes, stirring constantly. Add carrots; cook for 2 to 4 minutes or until glazed.

Stir-fried Broccoli & Carrots

1½ cups small broccoli florets
2 medium carrots, sliced thin
1 small onion, sliced
1 tablespoon olive oil
1/2 cup chicken broth
2 teaspoons ginger
¼ teaspoon salt
1 tablespoon water
garlic

Prepare a 12" skillet with olive oil; heat until hot. Add garlic and ginger; stir fry about 1 minute or until light brown. Add broccoli, carrots, and onion; stir fry for 5 minutes. Stir in broth. Cook and stir for 10 to 15 minutes or until vegetables are tender.

Carrots in Lemon-Basil Butter

2 medium carrots
1 tablespoon butter
1/8 teaspoon finely shredded lemon peel
1 pinch basil

Cut carrots into julienne strips. Boil carrots until tender; drain. In saucepan, combine butter, lemon peel and basil; heat on medium heat for 2 minutes. Add carrots and stir well. Serve.

Jalapeño & Ginger Carrots

4 cups peeled and shredded carrots
4 jalapeños (seeded and thinly sliced, crosswise)
2 tablespoon ginger root, finely shredded
3 tablespoons olive oil
2 teaspoon mustard seed
2 tablespoons freshly squeezed lime juice or apple cider vinegar
1 teaspoon honey
½ teaspoon salt
2 tablespoons chopped fresh cilantro
2 cups plain yogurt (optional)

Heat the oil in a large skillet over medium-high heat. Remove from heat, add mustard and cover. Jiggle the pan until the popping noise subsides. Uncover and add the ginger and jalapeños. Cook uncovered about 1 minute, or until the jalapeños soften.

Stir in the carrots and simmer, stirring frequently, until the carrots turn bright orange. Add the lime juice (or apple cider vinegar), honey and salt. Cook for 1 minute, stir in cilantro and remove from heat. Allow to cool, mix with yogurt (optional) and serve cold.

Ginger-Lemon Carrots

1 ¼ pound carrots, peeled and cut diagonally
1 teaspoon freshly grated lemon peel
¼ cup fresh lemon juice
2 teaspoons butter
2 teaspoons honey
1 teaspoon grated fresh ginger
¼ teaspoon salt

In a large skillet, submerge carrots in water and bring to a boil over medium-high heat. Cover and simmer until crisp-tender, about 3 minutes. Drain water and add remaining ingredients. Stir over medium-high heat until carrots are glazed, or 1-2 minutes.

Happy Carrots

2 pounds carrots, peeled and sliced
1 large onion, diced
1 medium green pepper, diced
4 stalks celery, diced
¼ cup olive oil
¼ cup apple cider vinegar
10 oz. tomato juice (may use V8 juice)
2 teaspoon mustard seed
Stevia to taste
salt and pepper to taste

Cook carrots in boiling water until just tender. Drain. In a separate pan, combine remaining ingredients. Heat and stir to a boil. Reduce heat, cover and simmer for 10 minutes. Pour over carrots. Serve dish hot, or refrigerate for use as a salad.

Dilled carrots

Substitute for pickles

1½ pounds baby carrots
2 cups water
2 cups apple cider vinegar
3 cloves peeled garlic
1 tablespoon red pepper flakes
1 tablespoon dill seeds
2 teaspoons salt
4 sprigs fresh dill (1 inch lengths, with stems)

Clean carrots with grapefruit seed extract. Heat water, apple cider vinegar, garlic, pepper flakes, dill seeds and salt in a large saucepan to a rolling boil. Add carrots and heat to simmering. Reduce heat and simmer covered for 10 minutes.

Using tongs, arrange carrots in hot sterilized pint jars. (To sterilize jars, submerge in water boil for 10 minutes; leave in hot water until ready to use.)

Ladle hot vinegar mixture into jars, covering carrots and distributing spices evenly. Tuck fresh dill between carrots. Cover jars tightly with new lids and allow to cool. Store in refrigerator 2 to 3 days.

Glazed carrots

2 pounds carrots, peeled and sliced
1 garlic clove, minced
1 ginger root, chopped fine
2 teaspoons olive oil
1 tablespoon honey
1½ cups chicken broth or water

Heat oil in a deep skillet and add garlic and ginger. Cook over medium heat for 30 to 60 seconds. Add remaining ingredients and cook over medium heat until all liquid evaporates and carrots are tender. Add water if liquid evaporates too quickly. Season to taste.

Baked Beets

unpeeled, whole beets, washed and with their tops removed
butter to taste
sour cream to taste
1 lime

Place beets on a tray and bake at 350 degrees for 1 hour. Let cool slightly and slip off skins. Mash and top with butter and/or sour cream. Spritz with lime juice just before serving.

Baked Eggplant

2 small eggplants, about 8 ounces each
½ cup onion, chopped
1 tomato, halved, seeded and diced
1 tablespoon chopped ham
1 tablespoon pine nuts
1 tablespoon parsley, chopped
2 teaspoons olive oil
½ teaspoon salt; 1/8 teaspoon pepper

Preheat oven to 400 degrees. Cut eggplants in half, lengthwise. Cut once more at ½ inch intervals, brush lightly with 1 teaspoon of olive oil and place, cut side down, on a baking sheet.

Bake until eggplant browns and is tender when pierced with a skewer, or about 1 to 2 minutes. Reduce oven temperature to 350 degrees. Remove baking sheet to a wire rack and turn eggplant halves so that they are cut-side up, to allow them to partially cool.

Combine onion and remaining olive oil in a large skillet. Cook until tender, stirring constantly for about 5 minutes. Blend in tomato, ham, pine nuts, parsley, salt and pepper. Cover and remove from heat.

Use a soup spoon to scoop out pulp from the partially cooled eggplant pieces, leaving cavities in their centers. Combine the removed pulp with the ham and tomato mixture, blending well. Fill eggplant "shells" with this mixture and bake for 10 minutes, or until filling is heated thoroughly.

Onion-sautéed Eggplant

1½ tablespoons olive oil

1 medium onion, chopped

1¾ pound small eggplants

salt and fresh-ground pepper to taste

one 14½-ounce can stewed tomatoes, preferably Italian style (with basil, garlic, & oregano), juice included

1 to 2 tablespoons shredded, fresh basil

1 cup plain yogurt

Cut eggplants crosswise into 3/8-inch slices. Heat oil in a large, heavy sauté pan or wide casserole dish. Add onions and sauté over medium heat for 2 minutes. Add eggplant, sprinkle with salt, and cook until eggplant is coated with onion mixture, stirring constantly. Cover and cook for 5 minutes, stirring once or twice. Add tomatoes and bring to a boil. Cover and cook over medium-low heat, stirring occasionally for 15-20 minutes, or until eggplant is tender. Stir in basil and pepper, top with yogurt and serve hot or cold. *Makes 4 servings.*

Lime-Pickled Red Onion

1 large red onion, thinly sliced

¼ cup fresh lime juice

2 tablespoons cilantro, chopped

2 teaspoons olive oil

½ teaspoon oregano

½ teaspoon salt

Combine all ingredients in a large bowl. Cover, let stand 1 to 3 hours and then refrigerate. *Can be made 2 days in advance.*

Beef,
Pork
&
Lamb

Beef, Pork & Lamb

Mmmmmmmmmmmmmmmmmmmmmmmmm! You haven't eaten fajitas until you've eaten these! For those of you who prefer not to eat meat, some of these recipes can easily substitute soy for the meat itself. For example, the lamb and summer squash dinner could be customized to become tofu and squash. For those who enjoy meat on occasion, you will find that store-bought meat is significantly different from grass fed meat, the latter being preferable.

Stewed Corned Beef

one 3-pound corned beef
water
1 teaspoon peppercorns, or 1/4 teaspoon pepper
6 whole cloves
1 bay leaf
6 carrots, halved lengthwise
1 medium-sized head of cabbage, cut into 6 wedges

Place beef in large saucepan or Dutch oven, covering with water. Add peppercorns, cloves and bay leaf. Bring to a boil. Reduce heat to low; cover and simmer 3-3½ hours or until tender. Add carrots, cover and simmer for 10 minutes. Add cabbage and cook 15 minutes, or until vegetables are tender. Remove bay leaf. To serve, cut beef into pieces and serve with cooking liquid and vegetables.

Makes 8 servings.

Stuffed Fillet of Beef

This recipe calls for a stuffing of roasted red peppers in a creamy mixture of spinach, herbs and goat cheese. The roast can be filled and tied well in advance so that all you have left to do is to roast the meat for an hour or less, before serving. When sliced open, the stuffing's red, green and white colors make this dish quite striking.

1¼ pounds spinach, stemmed and cleaned
8 ounces soft, creamy goat's cheese
½ teaspoon dried rosemary leaves, crushed
½ teaspoon dried thyme leaves
fresh-ground pepper
one 3-pound beef tenderloin, trimmed
salt
4 medium roasted red bell peppers
3 tablespoons olive oil
fresh-snipped chives or chopped parsley for garnish

Set aside 10-12 large spinach leaves. Blanch remaining leaves in boiling water until just wilted, about 2 minutes. Run under cold water in a strainer to cool. Drain well and place in a clean kitchen towel. Squeeze and wring out until all excess water is removed. Coarsely chop. Mix spinach, goat cheese, rosemary, thyme and ¼ teaspoon black pepper in a mixing bowl until well blended. Make a slit lengthwise down center of tenderloin, cutting two-thirds of the way through meat. Spread meat open and pound to a ½ inch thickness with a meat pounder. Season with salt and pepper.

Lay reserved, uncooked spinach leaves over meat, leaving an inch border all around and making an overlapping layer over meat. Next, make a layer of overlapping red peppers. Shape goat cheese and spinach mixture into a log the same length as meat and place over peppers. Finally, roll meat tightly at inch intervals with kitchen string. (Meat can be prepared several hours ahead to this point. Cover and refrigerate).

Preheat oven to 375 degrees. Heat oil in a large heavy skillet over medium-high heat and brown tenderloin well on all sides, about 5 minutes. Transfer meat to a rack set in a roasting pan. Salt and pepper generously. Roast about 45 minutes, or until meat turns pink inside. Check for doneness by making a slit with a small knife. Once the dish is done, remove it from oven and let it stand for 15 minutes. Cut and remove strings, and then cut meat into inch thick slices. Arrange on a warm serving platter, garnishing with a sprinkling of chives or parsley if desired.

Makes 8 servings.

Garlic Pepper Steak

4 beef shoulder top blade (flat iron) steaks (about 7 oz. each)
2 teaspoons chopped fresh thyme
2 large cloves garlic, minced
½ teaspoon pepper
2 teaspoons goat's cheese
salt

Combine thyme, garlic and pepper; press evenly onto beef steaks.

Place steaks on grid over medium, ash-covered coals. Grill, covered, 10 to 14 minutes for medium rare to medium doneness, turning once. During last two minutes of grilling, sprinkle with cheese. Season with salt to taste.

Italian Roast & Vegetables

one 2-pound beef eye round roast
½ teaspoon salt
½ teaspoon dried basil
½ teaspoon dried oregano
1/8 teaspoon pepper
3 medium-sized zucchini, sliced into 1/2 inch sections
2 yellow squash, sliced to same size
1 tablespoon olive oil
1 teaspoon lemon juice
½ teaspoon dried basil
½ cup cherry tomato halves

Preheat oven to 325 degrees. In a small bowl, combine salt, basil, oregano and pepper. Use mixture to season beef. Place roast on a rack in a shallow roasting pan. Insert an ovenproof meat thermometer so that its tip is centered in thickest part of beef. Do not add water or cover.

Roast at 325 degrees for 1½ hours for medium rare doneness. Remove when meat thermometer registers 135 degrees, transfer to board, tent with foil and let stand 15-20 minutes. The roast's temperature will continue to rise about 10 degrees to reach 145 degrees, or medium rare.

Increase oven temperature to 425 degrees. In a large bowl, toss all of the vegetables except for the tomatoes. Place on a rack in a pan and roast at 425 degrees for 15 minutes or until tender. Add tomatoes and toss once more. Carve roast and serve it together with the vegetables. Season with salt to taste.

Makes 4-6 servings.

Grilled Steaks with Rosemary

Marinated in garlic and lemon juice, these steaks are subtly seasoned with the flavor of the accompanying herbs.

2 boneless sirloin steaks (each about 1½ pounds and ¾ inch thick)
1 small bunch fresh rosemary
6 medium garlic cloves, peeled and smashed
1 teaspoon salt
½ teaspoon freshly ground black pepper
2 tablespoons lemon juice
6 tablespoons extra-virgin olive oil

With a sharp paring knife, make small slits about every inch over both surfaces of steaks. Remove leaves from 2-3 rosemary sprigs and insert 1-2 leaves in each slit. Place steaks in a shallow pan that will hold them in a single layer. Combine garlic, salt, pepper and lemon juice in a small bowl and mix well. Stir in oil and pour over meat. Cover with plastic wrap and marinate for 2-6 hours or overnight, turning several times.

To cook meat, remove from marinade. Arrange a rack 5 inches from heat source, spray rack with olive oil and preheat grill. When grill is ready, cook steaks until medium-rare, 3-5 minutes per side. Watch carefully, since cooking times will vary with type of grill and intensity of heat. Alternatively, broil steaks 4-5 inches from heat for 3-5 minutes per side. To serve, place steaks on a warm serving plate and garnish with a cluster of remaining rosemary sprigs. Cut each steak into 3 portions.

Makes 6 servings.

Steak Salad

1 pound beef top round steak, cut 1 inch thick
6 cups torn romaine lettuce
1 medium cucumber, thinly sliced
½ small red onion, cut into thin wedges
2 tablespoons crumbled feta cheese
8 black olives

Marinade

2/3 cup fresh lemon juice
1/3 cup olive oil
2 teaspoons dried oregano
½ teaspoon each salt and pepper

Whisk marinade ingredients in a small bowl. Place beef steak and half of marinade in a food-safe plastic bag, closing bag securely and turning to coat. Place in refrigerator 6 hours or overnight, turning occasionally. Set aside unused marinade.

Remove steak, discarding marinade. Place steak on rack in broiler pan so surface of beef is 2 to 3 inches from heat. Broil 17 to 18 minutes for medium rare doneness, turning once. Remove, let stand 10 minutes and then carve into slices.

Combine beef, lettuce, cucumber and onion in large bowl. Add reserved marinade and toss. Sprinkle with cheese and olives.

Makes 4 servings.

Garlic-smothered Rib Steaks

This dish features steaks slathered with chopped garlic and topped with sweet onions sautéed in Hungarian paprika.

5 tablespoons olive oil, plus extra if needed
2 large sweet onions, cut in half and thinly sliced
1 tablespoon sweet Hungarian paprika
8 garlic cloves, smashed & chopped finely, but not quite minced
two 2-inch thick rib steaks (about 2 pounds each)
salt and fresh-ground black pepper to taste

Heat 3 tablespoons olive oil in a large skillet over medium-high heat. Add onions, lower heat and sauté until golden brown, stirring often and adding more oil as needed (about 3 minutes). Stir in paprika and set aside. Pour remaining 2 tablespoons olive oil into a small saucepan. Add garlic and reserve.

Shortly before grilling, thoroughly clean surface of a gas grill with a metal brush, then coat surface evenly with olive oil. Heat grill until hot. Season steaks with salt and pepper. Grill for 8 minutes, turn and grill for 6 minutes more, or until desired doneness. Let steaks rest for 5-7 minutes. At the same time, heat garlic until oil is bubbling hot, then remove from heat. Reheat onions and season with salt. With slotted spoons, spread garlic, then onions, evenly over steaks. Carve in to thick slices. Serve on heated plates.

Makes 4 servings.

Brisket & Cabbage

one 2½ to 3 pound flat half beef brisket, trimmed
1 teaspoon black peppercorns
2 bay leaves
1 medium-large head cabbage, cut into 8 wedges

Place the brisket in a 6-quart pot or Dutch oven and add the juices from the package. Fill pot with enough water to cover the meat by a couple of inches, then add the peppercorns and bay leaves. Bring to a boil over high heat, and then reduce the heat to low. Skim off and discard any foam that rises to the surface. Cover and simmer for 2½ - 3 hours, or until the meat is very tender. Add enough water during cooking, as necessary, to keep the brisket covered with water. Remove the meat to a serving platter, reserving the liquid. Cover brisket loosely with foil and let it sit for 10 minutes.

Add the cabbage to the brisket cooking liquid, turning up the heat slightly to return the mixture to a boil. Reduce heat to low, cover and cook for about 10 minutes, or until the cabbage is tender. Remove and discard the bay leaves. To serve, slice the brisket thinly across the grain and serve hot, accompanied by the cabbage.

Makes 8 servings.

Goulash with Green Peppers

This dish features chunks of meat browned slowly and spiced with sweet Hungarian paprika. Try making it a day in advance of serving, as its flavor improves with reheating.

1½ pounds boneless beef chuck
2 strips bacon
2 medium sized onions, chopped
¾ cup beef broth
1½ tablespoon Hungarian sweet paprika
¾ teaspoon salt
1 small green pepper
sour cream

Cut beef into 1½ inch cubes. Dice the bacon and put into heavy Dutch oven. Sauté over medium high heat, add beef cubes. Brown slowly until richly browned on all sides. Add the onions. Cook 2-3 minutes or until onions are softened. Add the broth, paprika, salt and green pepper, blending well. Cook slowly, covered without allowing to boil, for about 2 hours or until meat is very tender but not soft. Add more liquid if needed — it should not be soupy. Add salt to taste, as needed. Serve with sour cream on the side.

Makes 4 servings.

Beef with Onions & Thyme

You can prepare this dish in advance, up to the stage in which the cooking liquid is strained. Return the strained liquid and beef to the pan and refrigerate for up to a day. When you are ready, skim the solid fat from the surface and continue with the recipe.

1 tablespoon fresh thyme, minced
1 large garlic clove, minced
1 3½-pound beef brisket, trimmed
2 teaspoons olive oil, divided
¾ teaspoon salt, divided
¼ teaspoon freshly ground black pepper
1½ cups chopped onion
1 cup chopped carrot
1 cup chopped celery
3 cups beef broth
¼ cup lemon juice
1 bay leaf
1 pound baby carrots with tops
1 pound pearl onions, peeled
2 tablespoons chopped fresh parsley
1 teaspoon chopped fresh thyme

Preheat oven to 350 degrees. Combine 1 tablespoon thyme and garlic. Make 12 small slits on the surface of the brisket and stuff each with about ¼ teaspoon of garlic mixture. Rub beef with 1 teaspoon oil, sprinkle it with another teaspoon and then dust it with ¼ teaspoon salt and ¼ teaspoon pepper.

Place a large ovenproof skillet over medium-high heat. Add beef, cooking on all sides until browned (about 2 minutes). Remove beef from pan, switching it out for the chopped onions, chopped carrot, and celery; sauté 6 minutes. Add ½ teaspoon salt, broth, lemon juice, and bay leaf, bringing it to a boil.

Return brisket to pan, cover and place in oven. Bake at 350 degrees for 1 hour. Reduce heat to 325 degrees and turn beef. Cover and bake for an additional 90 minutes or until tender, turning twice. Remove beef from pan.

Drain cooking liquid through a sieve into a bowl, pressing down on vegetables to extract liquid. Discard solids. Place a zip-top plastic bag inside a 2 cup glass measure. Pour drippings into bag and let it stand 10 minutes, allowing the fat to rise to the top. Seal the bag, carefully snip off one of its bottom corners and drain contents into a bowl. Stop before the fat layer reaches opening and discard the fat.

Trim all but 1 inch from green tops of baby carrots. Heat 1 teaspoon oil in a large skillet over medium-high heat. Add pearl onions and sauté until browned (about 3 minutes). Add beef, the cooking liquid from the preceding paragraph and the baby carrots. Bring to a boil. Return to roasting pan, cover and bake at 350 degrees for 1 hour, turning once. Sprinkle with parsley and a teaspoon of thyme. Serve the beef topped with the vegetable sauce, or with it on the side.

Make 8 servings.

Beef & Spinach Patties

This dish transforms your plain ground beef into tasty patties.

1 small onion, finely chopped
3 tablespoons butter
1 clove garlic
1 egg
1 pound ground beef
½ cup well drained, thawed frozen chopped spinach
½ cup beef broth
1 teaspoon salt
¼ teaspoon coarsely ground black pepper
chopped parsley for garnish

Sauté onion in 2 tablespoons of butter in a large frying pan, until soft and lightly browned. Remove from heat and mix in garlic.

Beat egg in a medium bowl. Blend in onion mixture, ground beef, spinach, 2 tablespoons beef broth, salt and pepper. Shape into 4 oval patties, each about 1 inch thick.

Add 1 tablespoon butter to same pan in which onions were cooked. Place patties in pan and brown over moderately high heat, about 4 minutes on each side, turning once. Remove patties to a warm platter to keep them warm.

Add remaining 6 tablespoons broth to pan. Cook, stirring to mix in pan drippings. Boil for about 30 seconds and pour over patties. Sprinkle with parsley.

Makes 4 servings.

Chili-Rubbed, Grilled Beef

2 tablespoons chili powder
3 teaspoons dried oregano leaves
1 teaspoon cumin
½ teaspoon salt
½ teaspoon pepper
¼ teaspoon onion powder
¼ teaspoon ground red pepper (cayenne)
1 pound boneless beef top sirloin steak (½ - ¾ inch thick)
¼ cup sour cream

Preheat grill. In a small bowl, combine all ingredients except beef and sour cream and mix well. Brush both sides of beef with water. Sprinkle spice mixture over both sides, in turn, rubbing the mixture into the beef with your fingers. Place beef on gas grill over medium-high heat and cover. Cook 9-12 minutes or until beef reaches desired doneness, turning once. Let stand 5 minutes before serving. To serve, cut beef diagonally into thin slices. Top each serving with 1 tablespoon of sour cream.

Makes 4 servings.

Beef-stuffed Peppers

This variation on a popular dish uses zucchini in place of the usual rice.

4 medium-sized green, red or yellow bell peppers

Stuffing

1 pound ground beef
¾ cup chopped onion
¼ cup zucchini, diced (raw)
3 tablespoons tomato paste
½ teaspoon salt
½ teaspoon dried oregano
¼ teaspoon black pepper

Sauce

1 can (14½ ounces) Italian-style tomatoes, undrained
1 tablespoon tomato paste
½ teaspoon dried oregano

Preheat oven to 350 degrees. Cut tops off peppers and remove seeds. In a large bowl, thoroughly combine ground beef, onion, zucchini, tomato paste, salt, oregano and black pepper. Spoon into bell peppers and place in an 8x8 inch baking dish.

Combine sauce ingredients and pour over peppers. Cover dish tightly with foil and bake at 350 degrees until beef is not pink inside and juices show no pink color (1-1/2 hours).

Makes 4 servings.

Salt-encrusted, Herbed Beef

Although encrusted in salt, the beef remains exceptionally moist and tender.

1/3 cup olive oil
¼ cup minced onion
1 teaspoon garlic salt
1 teaspoon dried basil
½ teaspoon dried marjoram
½ teaspoon dried thyme
¼ teaspoon ground black pepper
one 3-pound beef roast
3 pounds salt
1¼ cups water

Combine oil, onion, garlic salt, basil, marjoram, thyme, and pepper in a heavy plastic bag; mix well. Insert roast; coat well with marinade. Marinade in refrigerator 2 hours or overnight.

Preheat oven 350 degrees. Line roasting pan with foil. Make a thick paste with the salt and water. Shape 1 cup of the paste into a ½ inch thick rectangle in a pan. Pat roast dry with paper towels and place it atop the rectangle; pack remaining salt paste around meat to seal well. Bake for 60-70 minutes. Steam may cause crust to crack slightly. Remove from oven and let stand 10 minutes. Remove and discard salt crust.

Makes 8-10 servings.

Beef Fajitas

Two 1-pound steaks (skirt or flank cuts work best)
1/3 cup fresh lime juice
1/3 cup olive oil
4 large cloves garlic, minced
1½ teaspoons ground cumin
2 teaspoons cracked pepper
1 medium onion, sliced and separated into rings
1 tablespoon butter
salt and pepper to taste

Place steaks between two sheets of heavy-duty plastic wrap and use a meat mallet or rolling pin to gently pound them to an even thickness. Insert steaks into a heavy-duty, zip-lock plastic bag or a large, shallow dish. Combine lime juice, olive oil, garlic, cumin and cracked pepper, stirring well. Pour marinade over meat and seal or cover. Marinade in refrigerator for 8 hours, turning meat occasionally.

Remove steaks from marinade. Bring the marinade to a boil in a small sauce pan and set aside. Grill steaks over hot coals (400 to 500 degrees) 6-8 minutes on each side or to desired doneness, basting often with the marinade.

Place sliced onion and butter on a piece of heavy-duty foil; sprinkle with salt and pepper to taste. Wrap tightly and grill over medium-hot coals (350-400 degrees) for 5 minutes, or until tender.

Slice steaks diagonally across the grain into thin slices. Top each meat serving with guacamole and, if desired, with chopped tomato, sour cream and/or shredded lettuce.

Makes 8 servings.

Swiss Steak

1½ cups chopped onion
1 teaspoon minced garlic
2 pounds round steak
salt and pepper to taste
one 14½-ounce can whole tomatoes, chopped with their juices or one 8-ounce can of tomato sauce
one 16-ounce package of baby carrots
olive oil

In a large skillet coated with olive oil, sauté the onion and garlic over medium heat until tender. Trim round steak (if necessary) and season with salt and pepper. Add the meat to the skillet and brown on both sides for about 7 minutes. Add tomatoes, tomato sauce and carrots. Bring to a boil, reduce the heat and cook, covered, until the meat is very tender (about 1½ to 2 hours).

Beef Stroganoff

1 pound ground beef or turkey
1 medium onion, chopped
1 clove garlic, minced
1 cup beef broth
1 teaspoon sea salt
¼ teaspoon pepper
½ teaspoon thyme
fresh parsley, chopped
2 tablespoons olive oil

Heat oil in a wide frying pan over medium to high heat. Lightly brown the beef. Add onion and garlic, stirring until the onion becomes limp and translucent. Add the broth, salt, pepper, and thyme. Simmer, stirring frequently until thickened. Garnish with parsley. Serve with your favorite vegetable!

Carne Asada

1 teaspoon vegetable oil
6 ounces flank steak, cut in half, lengthwise
¼ teaspoon salt
½ teaspoon fresh garlic, chopped
2 small tomatoes, diced
½ small onion, diced
½ avocado, diced
chopped, fresh cilantro
1 jalapeño, chopped (spicy)

Heat oil in heavy large skillet over high heat. Sauté the garlic for 3 to 5 minutes. Add the steak to the skillet and cook until just cooked through, turning once, about 4 minutes. Add salt to taste. Transfer steak to a cutting board and cut into small pieces. Top with tomatoes, onion, avocado, cilantro and jalapeño pepper. Leave out the jalapeño for a less spicy meal.

Veal Chops with Artichoke

This dish features tender veal chops browned and then roasted with bell pepper slices and artichoke hearts.

four 6-ounce lean veal chops (3/4 inch thick)
1 teaspoon cracked black pepper
1/3 cup sliced green pepper
¾ cup sliced sweet orange, red and yellow pepper
1/3 cup chicken broth
¼ teaspoon dried whole thyme
2 cloves garlic, minced
one 14-ounce can artichoke hearts, drained and quartered
2 tablespoons chopped fresh parsley
olive oil

Trim fat from veal chops and rub in cracked pepper. Coat a large, ovenproof skillet with olive oil and place over medium-high heat until hot. Add chops and cook until browned (3-4 minutes on each side). Remove chops from skillet and set aside.

Wipe drippings from skillet with a paper towel. Place peppers, broth, thyme and garlic in skillet and bring to boil. Reduce heat and allow to simmer for 5 minutes. Stir in artichoke hearts. Return chops to skillet, basting them with the artichoke mixture. Cover and bake at 350 degrees for 25 minutes, or until veal is tender. Sprinkle with chopped parsley and serve immediately.

Makes 4 servings.

Pork Tenderloin

1 tablespoon coarsely cracked black pepper
2¼-pound pork tenderloin
¼ cup fresh parsley
1 tablespoon fresh chives
1 tablespoon tarragon leaves
1 teaspoon thyme

Preheat the oven to 425 degrees. Rub the pepper evenly over the tenderloin. Chop the herbs. On waxed paper, combine the herbs. Roll the tenderloin in the herb mixture to completely coat. Place tenderloin on roasting rack. Roast for 30 to 45 minutes. Carve into slices.

Pork Stir Fry

4 tablespoons beef broth
½ teaspoon minced garlic
½ teaspoon minced ginger
1 pound pork tenderloin, cut into ½ inch strips
4 cups shredded cabbage
½ teaspoon salt
½ teaspoon red pepper
8 green onions, chopped

Heat broth in a large nonstick frying pan or wok. Add garlic, ginger, and green onions. Add pork and cook until pink color is nearly gone. Mix in cabbage and cover, continue cooking until cabbage is tender. Season with salt and red pepper to taste.

Caribbean Pork Tenderloin

2 pork tenderloins (about 1 pound each) or 4 pork chops
1 habañero chile (cored, seeded, and ribs removed), minced
2 small garlic cloves, minced
2 bay leaves
3 tablespoons thyme leaves, chopped
1½ teaspoon paprika
1/8 teaspoon ground nutmeg
salt to taste

Toast the bay leaves to dry. Crumble the bay leaves and grind. Combine bay leaves with chile, garlic, thyme, paprika, nutmeg and salt to make rub. Pat the rub all over the tenderloin. Bake, turning once, at 350 degrees until pink color of pork is nearly gone.

Basil Pork Chops

4 pork chops (1 1/4 lbs.)
1 cup tomato juice (may substitute V-8 juice)
1 tablespoon basil
1/2 teaspoon salt
1 teaspoon coarsely ground black pepper

In a large frying pan, brown chops. When chops are browned, add other ingredients. Cover tightly and simmer 40 minutes or until tender. Turn meat occasionally and add a few tablespoons of water if necessary to prevent burning.

Tomato Onion Pork Chops

4 pork chops
1 medium onion, chopped
8 ounces tomato juice (may substitute V-8)
1 tablespoon fresh basil, chopped
¼ cup honey
1 teaspoon mustard powder
salt and pepper to taste

Brown chops in a nonstick skillet over medium heat, turning occasionally. Continue cooking until golden; Remove chops. Add remaining ingredients to skillet, stirring constantly until it comes to a boil. Return chops to skillet; reduce heat and simmer for 20 minutes. Spoon the sauce over chops.

Mustard Pork Chops

5 ounces boneless pork chop
1 thick slice onion
¼ teaspoon olive oil
¼ teaspoon rosemary
1 teaspoon mustard powder
salt and pepper to taste

Preheat oven to 350 degrees. Tear heavy-duty foil to make a 12 inch square and smear with olive oil. Place onion slice on half of foil. Spread both sides of pork chop with mustard powder, place it on the onion, sprinkle with salt and pepper and top with rosemary. Close foil, roll edges to firmly seal. Place in a baking pan and bake 20 to 30 minutes, or until pork chop is no longer pink in the center.

Pork Ribs

2 slabs baby back ribs
2 large white onions, chopped
1 large bunch celery, chopped
½ cup of olive oil
4 whole tomatoes, diced
24 oz. tomato juice (may substitute V8)
4 tablespoons honey
1 teaspoon each salt and pepper
½ teaspoon cinnamon

Partially precook ribs in a 450 degree oven for 45 minutes to 1 hour. Sauté the onions and celery in olive oil for 10 minutes. Add the remaining ingredients. Cook for a 30 minutes. Cut ribs into pieces and add to the mixture. Cook over medium heat for several hours. Serve and enjoy!

Baby-back Ribs

1 slab baby back ribs, seasoned with salt and pepper.
2 tablespoons honey
Homemade Barbeque Sauce

Preheat oven to 300 degrees. Bake on foil covered pan for 2½ hours. Add Homemade Barbeque Sauce and honey. Roast an additional half hour. Serve and enjoy!

Garlic Ribs

3 pounds pork spareribs
½ cup butter
1 teaspoon garlic, minced
juice of 1 lemon
½ teaspoon oregano

Preheat oven to 350 degrees. Combine butter and garlic. Rub ¾ of garlic mixture on both sides of ribs. Squeeze lemon juice all over ribs. Sprinkle oregano over ribs. Bake at 350 degrees for 45 minutes to 1 hour. Spread remaining mixture over ribs. Continue cooking for 5 minutes.

Honey-glazed Ribs

4 pounds pork spareribs
½ cup honey
¼ cup lemon juice
2 teaspoons grated lemon peel
2 teaspoons grated ginger
1 clove garlic, minced
1 teaspoon rosemary, crushed
½ teaspoon crushed red chilies
½ teaspoon ground sage
salt and pepper to taste

Preheat oven to 450 degrees. Cover spareribs with water in a large pot. Bring to a boil, reduce heat to medium and cook uncovered for about 5 minutes. Drain liquid. Season both sides of spareribs with salt and pepper. Place spareribs on a rack in roasting pan. Cover loosely with foil and bake for 15 minutes.

To make glaze, combine remaining ingredients, mixing well. Reduce oven temperature to 350 degrees. Brush spareribs with glaze and bake until fully cooked, about 1 hour, brushing with glaze every 15 minutes.

Salsa Spareribs

8 pounds pork spareribs
6 large, firm ripe tomatoes, diced
8 mild green chilies, diced
3 cloves garlic, minced
1 cup sour cream
1 tablespoon olive oil
1/8 cup apple cider vinegar
¼ cup chopped cilantro
4 limes, cut into wedges
salt and pepper to taste

Sauté diced tomatoes and chilies in skillet over medium heat. Place tomatoes and chilies in bowl. Add garlic, cilantro, vinegar and salt and pepper to taste. Spread mixture evenly over both sides of ribs.

Wrap ribs in foil and bake for 1 hour or until tender at 400 degrees. To serve, cut rib portions and garnish with lime wedges. Serve with "Zesty Salsa Dip" and sour cream.

Spareribs & Apples

5 pounds meaty spareribs
3 tablespoon butter
2 small onions, diced
1 carrot, shredded
3 green apples, sliced
½ tablespoon honey
salt and pepper to taste

Preheat oven to 350 degrees. In skillet, lightly brown spareribs in butter. Remove ribs from heat and place in aluminum foil. Add remaining ingredients to skillet and sauté until tender. Remove mixture from heat and add to ribs. Cover with foil and bake for 1 hour and 45 minutes.

Vegetable Ham

2 cups diced ham
2 tablespoons minced onion
1 cup zucchini, shredded
½ cup carrots, shredded
½ cup broccoli florets, sliced
1 tablespoon olive oil

Heat oil; brown ham, onion, and zucchini in heavy skillet. Add ½ cup water and vegetables; cover. Bring to a boil. Reduce heat and simmer until vegetables are just tender, about 6 to 10 minutes.

Stuffed, Baked Ham

Fully cooked half of a ham (about 10 pounds)
½ cup kale
½ to 1 cup chopped spinach
1 large onion, peeled
¾ cup watercress
½ cup celery leaves
½ teaspoon salt
¼ teaspoon pepper

Glaze:
½ cup honey
2 tablespoons apple cider vinegar
1 teaspoon mustard powder
2 teaspoons ginger

Preheat oven to 325 degrees. Cut rind and all but about ¼ inch of fat from ham. With a small, sharp knife, make X shaped incisions about 2 inches deep and 1 inch apart all over the fatty side.

In a food processor, pulse kale, spinach, onion, watercress, celery leaves, salt and pepper until finely chopped. Press into ham's X-shaped incisions, packing it in tightly. Place the ham, fat side up, in a shallow baking pan and bake for 2 hours.

Stir together honey, vinegar, mustard powder and ginger and brush mixture onto ham. Continue baking for 30 minutes, until ham is richly glazed. Remove ham from the oven and allow to cool for 20 minutes, for easier carving. Carve carefully, holding the slices to keep stuffing in place.

Lamb & Summer Squash

Lamb blocks are double-thick chops taken from the shoulder or hip.

4 lamb chops, about 1½ inches thick
1½ tablespoons olive oil
1 medium onion, thinly sliced
2 cloves garlic, minced or pressed
1 teaspoon salt
½ teaspoon dried oregano leaves
1/8 teaspoon pepper
1 cup chicken broth
2 medium zucchini and 2 crookneck squash, sliced into half-inch pieces
2 eggs
2 tablespoons lemon juice
2 green onions, thinly sliced (use part of tops) for garnish

In hot oil in a large, deep frying pan, brown lamb chops on both sides. Add onion, garlic, salt, oregano, pepper and broth. Bring to a boil, cover and reduce heat. Simmer until lamb is tender, 1 to 1½ hours. Add squash and cover again and simmer until it is just tender, 10 to 12 minutes. Using a slotted spoon, transfer lamb and vegetables to a warm serving dish. Keep warm.

In a bowl, beat eggs and lemon juice until well blended. Skim fat from top of cooking liquid and discard. Slowly add cooking liquid to egg mixture, beating with a whisk until well blended. Return mixture to pan and cook over low heat, stirring until sauce thickens (do not boil). Add salt to taste.

Pour sauce over lamb and vegetables and top with green onions. *Makes 4 servings.*

Skewered Lamb

This dish features a marinade of olive oil, lime juice and garlic, plus a final spritz of fresh lime. Cumin rounds out the medley of flavors.

½ cup olive oil
juice of 2 limes, plus 3 limes cut in half
3 plump garlic cloves, pressed
2½ pounds boneless leg of lamb, cut into 2 inch cubes
2 tablespoons medium-hot chile powder
1 tablespoon garlic powder
1 tablespoon cumin seeds
1 tablespoon salt
yogurt mixed with chopped mint

Three to six hours before serving, blend olive oil, lime juice, and garlic in a large bowl. Toss with meat to coat thoroughly.

Heat a small skillet over high heat. Add cumin seeds and stir until seeds are dark brown and fragrant. Remove from heat and transfer to a plate to cool. Grind toasted cumin in a spice grinder or with a mortar and pestle. (If using pre-ground cumin, do not toast or grind.) Pour the resultant powder into a small bowl. Stir in chile powder, garlic powder and salt.

Remove meat from marinade and dry gently with paper towels. Divide lamb among 8 skewers and sprinkle evenly with spice mixture. Let stand for 1 hour. Thoroughly clean surface of a gas grill with metal brush; then coat surface evenly with olive oil. Heat grill on high heat. Place skewers on rack and grill for 4 minutes each side, sprinkling meat generously with spice mixture several times while grilling. Transfer skewers to a large platter. Squeeze lime juice over meat, top with minted yogurt and serve.

Makes 4 servings.

Herbed Lamb Chops

This dish features loin chops infused with the flavor of fresh, minced herbs. Two chops are usually required to make one serving.

four 4-ounce lamb loin chops
¼ teaspoon salt
½ teaspoon freshly ground pepper
2 tablespoons minced fresh chives
2 tablespoons minced fresh parsley
2 tablespoons chopped fresh rosemary
1 tablespoon olive oil

Trim chops and sprinkle them with salt and pepper. Combine chives, parsley, and rosemary; press herb mixture on each side of chops. Heat oil in a nonstick skillet over medium-high heat. Add chops and cover to cook for 13 minutes on each side, or to desired doneness.

Makes 2 servings.

Chicken
&
Turkey

Chicken and Turkey

Poultry is an excellent source of amino acids (the building blocks of protein) and of protein itself! The creativity with which this section treats these sometimes less-than-exciting birds may make once "boring" chicken a new favorite at your house. Remember, grass-fed poultry is more nutritious than corn-fed, and it minimizes your exposure to the mycotoxins in corn.

Garlic & Rosemary Chicken

2 heads garlic, minced (½ cup)
1 cup fresh lemon juice (6 lemons)
2/3 cup fresh rosemary sprigs, coarsely chopped
1 tablespoon salt
1½ teaspoon freshly ground pepper
2 cups olive oil
3 broiler-fryers cut up (2½ to 3 pounds)
3 lemons, sliced
fresh rosemary sprigs to garnish

Combine spices and lemon juice, stirring until well blended. Gradually add oil, stirring with a wire whisk. Pour mixture evenly into three large heavy-duty, zip-top plastic bags. Add chicken pieces and lemon slices. Seal bags and marinate in refrigerator at least 8 hours, turning the bags occasionally.

Grease two roasting pans. Remove chicken from marinade, reserving the liquid. Arrange chicken in pans. Drizzle with the marinade and top with lemon slices. Bake uncovered at 425 degrees for 1 hour or until done, basting with pan juices every 20 minutes.

Makes 12 servings.

Roasted Lemon-Herb Chicken

This makes for an easy dinner. Just squeeze lemon over the bird, rub in the spices and baste it once or twice while it's in the oven. Add some chunks of vegetables to roast alongside during the last 30 minutes.

1 large lemon
1 broiler-fryer (3 to 3½ pounds)
several sprigs of thyme (or rosemary or oregano)
1 tablespoon lemon-pepper seasoning
1 tablespoon chopped fresh thyme (or rosemary or oregano)
olive oil

Slice lemon in half and squeeze juice over chicken. Insert lemon halves and thyme sprigs into the bird's body cavity. Brush chicken with olive oil and rub it with the lemon-pepper seasoning and chopped spices. Place chicken breast side up on a greased rack in broiler pan, or on a vertical roasting rack. Roast at 400 degrees for 45 minutes or until desired doneness, basting once or twice with drippings from the pan.
Makes 4 servings.

Grilled Chicken with Basil

Despite its simplicity, this dish delivers a complex mix of flavors. Use bone-in chicken breasts or meaty thighs.

3 tablespoons lemon juice
2 tablespoons chopped fresh basil (dried basil 2 teaspoons)
1 clove garlic, minced
¼ cup olive oil
4 skinned, bone-in chicken breast halves, or 8 skinned chicken thighs

Mix juice, basil and garlic in a blender for 30 seconds. With blender running, gradually add oil. Process until blended and set aside 1/4 of a cup. Brush chicken with remaining basil mixture; cover and marinate in refrigerator for 30 minutes. Grill chicken (covered with grill lid) at 300-350 degrees for 30 minutes or until done, basting twice with reserved basil mixture.

Makes 4 servings.

Roast Chicken with Rosemary

The rosemary infuses the chicken with a wonderful aroma.

one 3 to 3½ pound chicken, rinsed, with giblets removed
6 sprigs fresh rosemary, plus a few more for garnish
1 to 2 tablespoon extra-virgin olive oil
salt and fresh-ground pepper to taste

Preheat oven to 400 degrees. Pull out fat from inside chicken and place bird in a small roasting pan. Stuff chicken with 3 rosemary sprigs. Pour oil over chicken and sprinkle it with salt and a small amount of pepper. Rub the oil and spices into chicken. Add 3 more rosemary sprigs to pan, tucking them under the chicken. Roast chicken uncovered, basting once or twice, until chicken juices run clear when thickest part of thigh is pierced with a thin knife or skewer (about 1 hour).

Remove cooked rosemary from chicken and from the pan. Carve chicken and place pieces on a platter. Garnish with fresh rosemary sprigs. Skim excess fat from juices left in roasting pan, tasting and adding spices as necessary. When serving, spoon some of this juice over chicken.

Makes 4 servings.

Chicken in Pepper Sauce

This dish features spicy chicken in a colorful, grilled pepper and tomato sauce.

Roasted Pepper Sauce with Tomatoes and Garlic
(see Dressings, Dips and Sauces section)

2½ to 3 pounds chicken pieces, patted dry
1 to 2 tablespoons olive oil
1 large onion, sliced
2 large cloves garlic, chopped
¼ cup minced fresh cilantro
salt and fresh-ground pepper to taste
½ teaspoon ground cumin
½ teaspoon paprika
1 cup water
fresh cilantro sprigs

Prepare pepper sauce.

Combine salt, pepper, cumin, and paprika in a small bowl. Heat olive oil in a heavy stew pan or Dutch oven. Add onion, garlic, and cilantro to the oil and cook over medium-low heat, stirring frequently for 5 minutes.

Add chicken (skins removed if you like) and sprinkle with the paprika mixture. Cover and cook for 3 minutes.

Pour water into side of pan (not over chicken) and bring to a boil. Cover and simmer over low heat for 20 minutes, turning chicken occasionally. Use tongs to transfer the chicken pieces to a plate. Boil onion mixture left in pan uncovered, until it thickens. The liquid will reduce to about ½ cup.

Return chicken to stew pan and add roasted pepper sauce. Cover and cook over low heat, turning chicken pieces occasionally, 20-30 minutes or until chicken is tender. Season to taste. Serve hot or cold, garnished with cilantro.

Makes 4 servings.

Pepper Blackened Chicken

5 boneless, skinless chicken breasts
¼ teaspoon cayenne pepper
¾ teaspoon paprika
¼ teaspoon white pepper
¼ teaspoon salt (optional)
1 ¼ teaspoon thyme
1 ¼ teaspoon basil

Combine spices on a small plate. Roll breasts in the mixture, coating them on both sides and setting them aside on a large plate. For a milder chicken, cut the amount of spice. Grill chicken on a cast-iron pancake griddle (or barbecue, broil, or bake) until cooked through. Avoid overcooking. Top each breast with salsa.

Makes 5 servings.

Chicken Thighs with Onions

This dish features chicken cooked with lots of onions and green olives plus several herbs and spices, for a sensational flavor combination.

2½ pounds chicken thighs, patted dry
salt and fresh-ground pepper to taste
1½ teaspoons ground cumin
1 teaspoon paprika
2 tablespoons olive oil
1½ pounds onions (about 3 large), halved and thinly sliced
1 cup chicken stock
2 large cloves garlic, chopped
¼ teaspoon hot red pepper flakes
½ cup black olives, pitted
strained fresh lemon juice to taste (about 1 tablespoon)
2 tablespoons chopped fresh Italian parsley

Sprinkle chicken pieces with pepper on both sides. Mix the pepper with a teaspoon of the cumin and a half teaspoon of the paprika. Sprinkle the mixture over the chicken, using your fingers to rub the spices into the pieces.

Heat oil in large deep sauté pan. Add half the chicken thighs and lightly brown them over medium heat (about 2 minutes per side). Remove to a plate. Brown remaining chicken pieces and remove.

Add onions to pan. Cook over medium-low heat, stirring often, about 15 minutes or until onions soften. If pan appears to be drying out, cover onions as they cook.

Return chicken to pan, along with any juices that have pooled on the plate. Add stock, garlic, pepper flakes, as well as the remaining ½ teaspoon of cumin and ½ teaspoon of paprika. Cover and simmer 30 minutes, turning pieces once or twice. Add olives and cover and simmer 5-10 more minutes, or until chicken is tender. Add lemon juice to sauce and season to taste. Sprinkle chicken with parsley and serve hot.

Makes 4 servings.

Pollo de Lemon

4 boneless, skinless chicken breasts
3 tablespoons fresh lemon juice
1 tablespoon grated lemon peel
1 clove garlic, minced
2 to 3 teaspoons thyme
½ teaspoon salt (optional)
½ teaspoon freshly ground black pepper
1 lemon, thinly sliced

Place chicken in a bowl or casserole dish. Combine lemon juice, lemon peel and spices and pour over chicken. Marinate chicken in refrigerator for at least 3 hours.

Preheat oven to 350 degrees. Remove chicken from marinade and place in shallow baking dish. Pour marinade over chicken and bake for 30-45 minutes or until cooked through. Garnish with lemon slices.

Makes 4 servings.

Lemon-Garlic Chicken Thighs

In this dish, the sweet tomatoes contrast nicely with the lemony chicken. To get the outsides of the chicken thighs super crispy while still keeping the meat inside juicy, bake the chicken on a rack at high temperature, with the skins left on. Use a cooling rack placed in a shallow pan for perfect results. You can always remove the skins before eating.

8 chicken thighs
juice of 1 lemon
1 clove garlic, crushed
½ teaspoon, dried thyme leaves
white pepper to taste
10 cherry tomatoes
2 tablespoons butter

Combine lemon juice, garlic and thyme. Wash and pat dry chicken, placing it in a bowl. Toss the thighs with the lemon juice mixture, making sure all sides are coated. Leave chicken and juice mixture in bowl and refrigerate for 2 hours or more, turning pieces at least once.

Place thighs on a rack in the baking pan, skin side up. Sprinkle with salt and pepper. Bake at 425 degrees for about 30 minutes.

Halve the cherry tomatoes. Melt butter in a skillet and add the tomatoes, cooking 1 to 2 minutes to heat through.

Place chicken on serving platter, topped and surrounded with sautéed tomatoes. Serve immediately.
Makes 4 servings.

Chicken Fajitas

4 boneless, skinless chicken breasts

Marinade

2 cloves garlic, minced
1½ teaspoons cumin
½ teaspoon salt (optional)
3 tablespoons fresh lime juice

Tomato salsa

1 pound tomatoes, chopped
1 small onion, minced
1 fresh chili pepper, sliced thin
1 tablespoon fresh lime juice

Sautéed vegetables

1 clove garlic, minced
1 large onion, sliced
1 green pepper, sliced
1 red or yellow sweet pepper, sliced
1 tablespoon olive oil

Place chicken breasts in a bowl. Combine marinade ingredients and pour over chicken. Marinate in refrigerator for at least 30 minutes. Combine tomato salsa ingredients and refrigerate until ready to use. Sauté onion, garlic, and peppers in olive until soft. Set aside. Grill or broil chicken breasts until cooked through. Slice into strips.

Crisp Roasted Chicken

This dish features a stuffing of lemon, herbs and roasted garlic, as well as a lemon-garlic sauce. The super hot, cast-iron skillet is the secret to making the chicken as crisp as it can be.

1 head garlic, cut in half diagonally
3 tablespoons olive oil
2 teaspoons water
one 3½ to 4 pound frying chicken
salt and fresh-ground pepper to taste
2 lemons, cut in halves
2 large fresh rosemary leaves (dried 1 teaspoon)
1 lg branch fresh lemon verbena or lemon balm, if available
5 branches fresh herbs *(thyme, basil, p.apple sage etc.)*
½ cup chicken stock
1 tablespoon minced fresh flat-leaf parsley
more fresh herbs for garnish

Preheat oven to 325 degrees. Place garlic on a large square of foil and drizzle with 1 tablespoon oil. Then drizzle each half with 1 teaspoon water. Verify oven temperature. Seal garlic inside foil and roast for 45 minutes. Remove packet from oven, open and allow to cool somewhat. Garlic will still be firm.

Increase oven temperature to 475 degrees. Pour any oil from garlic packet into a 10 to 12-inch cast-iron skillet. Add enough oil to thoroughly oil skillet. Rub the inside of the cavity of the chicken with salt and pepper. Insert garlic halves and 1 lemon half into the cavity. Then pack in the herbs. Transfer chicken to the skillet, breast side up.

Rub chicken with remaining 2 tablespoons of olive oil. Squeeze juice of second lemon half over it. Rub surface with salt and pepper. Roast the chicken, basting once with third lemon half, for 60 minutes, or until meat is exceptionally tender when pierced with a fork — juices should run clear.

Transfer chicken to a carving board. Using a heavy pot holder, transfer skillet to stove. Over high heat, whisk in chicken stock and juice of remaining lemon half, scraping up any browned bits that stick to skillet. To thicken sauce, bring to a rapid boil 2-3 times. Skim off surface fat and season to taste with salt and pepper. Cover to keep warm.

Remove garlic and herbs from cavity of chicken. Squeeze garlic cloves from their skins and mash them; add garlic to sauce, whisking well to blend.

Cut chicken into quarters. Blend any accumulated juices into gravy and heat thoroughly. Transfer chicken quarters to heated serving plates. Sprinkle with parsley and garnish lavishly with fresh herbs. Serve with sauce.

Makes 4 servings.

Paprika Chicken

4 pounds bone-in skinless chicken breast, thighs and legs
½ teaspoon salt
½ teaspoon coarsely ground black pepper
1 teaspoon garlic powder
olive oil
2 medium-sized yellow onions
1 cup tomato juice
1 tablespoon plus 1 teaspoon ground paprika
2 tablespoons finely chopped fresh parsley

Rinse the chicken and pat dry with paper towels. Combine salt, pepper and garlic powder and sprinkle over pieces. Coat a large skillet with olive oil and cook chicken for about 2 minutes or until nicely browned on the bottom. Lightly brush the tops of the pieces with olive oil, turn and cook for another couple of minutes, or until nicely browned on both sides.

Thinly slice the onions and separate them into rings. Coat an 11 by 13 inch roasting pan (or the bottom of a broiler pan) with olive oil and arrange half of the onion rings over the bottom of the pan. Place the chicken on the bed of onions and cover it with the remaining onion rings.

Cover the pan tightly with foil and bake at 400 degrees for 30 minutes. Carefully remove the foil (steam will escape), baste the chicken with the pan juices, and bake for an additional 20-25 minutes, or until the chicken is tender and no longer pink inside. Transfer the chicken to a serving platter, drizzle the pan juices over the top and sprinkle with the parsley. Serve hot.

Makes 8 servings.

Chicken in Red Pepper Sauce

4 slices of bacon
four 4-ounce skinned and de-boned chicken breast halves
¼ teaspoon salt
¼ teaspoon black pepper
½ cup chopped red onion
½ teaspoon ground coriander
3 garlic cloves, minced
1 can diced chipotle chile in adobo sauce, drained
1 cup salsa
one 7-ounce bottle roasted red bell peppers, drained and sliced

Fry bacon in a large skillet over medium-high heat until crisp. Remove from skillet, crumble and set aside. Sprinkle chicken with salt and pepper. Add chicken to bacon drippings left in skillet and sauté 2 minutes on each side. Remove chicken to a plate. Fill skillet with onion, coriander, garlic and chile, and sauté for 3 minutes. Stir in salsa and bell peppers and return chicken to pan, as well. Cover and cook over medium heat 12 minutes or until chicken is done. Sprinkle with crumbled turkey bacon and garnish with cilantro.

Makes 4 servings.

Curried Chicken

Moist chicken in a spicy curry sauce goes well with popular curry side dishes such as plain yogurt, chopped cucumber and toasted almonds.

one 3 to 3½ pound chicken, split into legs, breast, thighs etc.
salt to taste
1 tablespoon butter
1 medium-sized onion, finely chopped
1 clove garlic, minced or pressed
2 teaspoon curry powder
¼ teaspoon ground ginger
1 tablespoon tomato paste
1 cup chicken broth
chopped parsley for garnish

Sprinkle chicken pieces with salt. In a large frying pan, heat butter and brown chicken well, a few pieces at a time, on all sides. Remove chicken pieces as they brown and set them aside. Add butter to pan and spoon in onion. Constantly stir over medium heat until soft and just beginning to brown. Add garlic and curry powder and continue stirring for 1 minute. Mix in ginger and tomato paste and return chicken to pan.

Pour chicken broth over chicken and bring to a boil. Cover and reduce heat, simmering chicken until it is tender (about 45 minutes). Remove chicken pieces to a warm serving dish. Sprinkle with parsley.

Makes 4 servings.

Spicy Chicken

This easy yet delicious recipe can be prepared in less than 30 minutes. You can adjust its spiciness by changing the varieties and amounts of chili powder and hot peppers you use.

2 skinless, boneless chicken breast halves
1 tablespoon chili powder (divided)
salt and pepper to taste
1 tablespoon olive oil
1 cup chopped green bell pepper
½ cup chopped onion
2 jalapeño peppers, seeded and minced
1 large tomato cut into chunks
10 drops hot sauce

Cut chicken into bite-sized pieces and season with ½ tablespoon chili powder, salt and pepper. Heat oil in a large skillet over medium-high heat and sauté chicken for 3-4 minutes, or until no longer pink. Remove from skillet with a slotted spoon and keep warm. In the same skillet, stir fry bell pepper and onion until soft. Add jalapeño peppers, tomatoes, the remaining ½ tablespoon chile powder and the hot pepper sauce. Cook, stirring continuously, for an additional 3-5 minutes. Add chicken and stir fry for 2 minutes.

Makes 2 servings.

Boneless Garlic Chicken

This tasty dish features chicken breasts sautéed in garlic and onion.

3 tablespoons butter
4 skinless, boneless chicken breast halves
2 teaspoons garlic powder
1 teaspoon seasoning salt
1 teaspoon onion powder

Melt butter in a large skillet over medium high heat. Add chicken and sprinkle with garlic powder, seasoning salt and onion powder. Sauté for about 10-15 minutes on each side, or until chicken is cooked through and juice runs clear.

Makes 4 servings.

Chicken with Cheese Stuffing

This recipe works great served with your favorite Italian herb pasta sauce and a nice, green salad.

4 ounces goat's cheese, softened
3 tablespoons thinly sliced basil
1 tablespoon minced garlic
4 (6 ounces) skinless, boneless chicken breast halves
1 jar Sun Dried Pasta Sauce
3 whole garlic cloves

Combine goat cheese, 2 tablespoons basil and minced garlic. Set aside. Place chicken breast halves between 2 sheets of heavy-duty plastic wrap, and pound each half to a ¼-inch thickness using a meat mallet or rolling pin. Divide the cheese mixture evenly among breast halves. Roll up in jelly-roll fashion and tuck in sides, securing each roll with wooden picks.

Heat the pasta sauce and whole garlic cloves in a large skillet over medium heat. Add chicken, cover and cook 25 minutes, or until chicken is done. Garnish dish with basil and serve with a green salad.

Makes 4 servings.

Chicken Breast in Sour Cream

4 tablespoons butter, melted
6 chicken breast halves (about 3 pounds)
1 tablespoon olive oil
½ cup celery, chopped
½ bell pepper, chopped
1 zucchini or squash, chopped
1 cup sour cream
1 teaspoon salt
½ cup onion, chopped
¼ teaspoon pepper

Sauté chicken in butter until lightly browned. Arrange chicken in a lightly greased (with olive or coconut oil) casserole dish. Set aside. Sauté onion, celery, zucchini (or squash) and bell pepper in olive oil until tender. Remove from heat and let cool slightly. Combine the vegetables, sour cream, salt and pepper. Spoon mixture over chicken. Cover and bake at 350 degrees for 45 to 55 minutes, until chicken is cooked through.

Baked Barbeque Chicken

1 (2 to 3 pounds) whole chicken, cut into pieces
2 teaspoons garlic powder
1 ½ cups prepared Homemade Barbeque Sauce

Preheat oven to 350 degrees. Place chicken in a shallow baking dish and sprinkle with garlic powder. Cover and bake 1 hour at 350 degrees. Remove baking dish from oven and drain any fat from dish. Pour the barbeque sauce evenly over the chicken and bake uncovered for 30 minutes at 350 degrees. Remove and serve.

Turkey & Artichoke Roll-ups

This dish is great as a quick snack or as an appetizer.

two 6-ounce jars marinated and quartered artichoke hearts
4 pounds thinly sliced, pre-roasted turkey breast

Drain the artichokes, reserving the marinade. Cut the turkey into ¾-inch wide strips. Wrap a strip of turkey around each artichoke quarter, and secure with a wooden toothpick. Place the artichoke pieces in a shallow baking dish, and add 2 tablespoons of the reserved marinade to the dish. Bake at 350 degrees for 15 minutes, or until heated through. Transfer to a serving tray, and serve hot.

Makes 24 rollups.

Paprika Turkey Thighs

Turkey thighs sometimes make more sense than a whole bird because you can buy just enough to feed your family — without all the leftovers to worry about. This dish can be prepared ahead of time. Simply store the thighs and the sauce separately and refrigerate. Reheat and add sour cream just before serving.

4 small turkey thighs
3 large onions, chopped
4 tablespoons butter
1 tablespoon salt
2 tablespoons paprika
fresh-ground pepper to taste
1 clove garlic, minced or pressed
1 green pepper, cut into inch squares
2 cups chicken broth or stock
1 cup sour cream

Wash and pat turkey thighs dry. Remove their skins and cut the thighs into halves. Sauté onions in the butter until transparent, 2-3 minutes. Add turkey thighs, salt, paprika, pepper and garlic. Add green pepper and broth. Cover.

Simmer slowly until turkey is tender, 1-1½ hours. Check and add more liquid if needed. Remove thighs. Bring sauce to a boil. Cook until reduced to approximately 2 cups. Stir in sour cream, pour over thighs and serve immediately.

Makes 4 servings.

Spicy Turkey Patties

You can grill this dish, but the patties will stay more moist if you sauté them. Top them with Herb Salsa (see dressings and dips section).

4 large cloves garlic, pressed
2 teaspoons ground coriander
1 teaspoon ground cumin
½ teaspoon freshly ground pepper
pinch of cayenne pepper
¼ teaspoon salt (optional)
1 ¼ pounds ground turkey
2 tablespoons olive oil

Mix spices in a bowl. Add turkey and mix lightly to blend. Shape into 4 patties.

Heat olive oil in a medium-sized fry pan. Add patties and cook over medium heat until they are springy when pressed (about 3 minutes on each side). Serve immediately.

Makes 4 servings.

Turkey in Savory Pepper Sauce

Thoroughly browning the onions in this dish gives the sauce its rich, brown hue. For an extra spiciness, add extra hot paprika or cayenne.

one 1½ pound boneless turkey breast roast
salt and fresh-ground pepper to taste
2 to 3 tablespoons olive oil
2 large onions, sliced
¾ chicken stock or broth
1 large green bell pepper, diced (¾ to 1 inch)
1 large red bell pepper, diced (¾ to 1 inch)
3 large cloves garlic, chopped
1 tablespoon sweet paprika
hot paprika or cayenne pepper to taste (¼ to ½ teaspoon)
one 14½-ounce can diced tomatoes, drained

Heat oil in a large, heavy stew pan over medium heat. Sprinkle turkey with salt and pepper. Place breast in pan and brown lightly on all sides. Remove to a plate.

Add onions to pan and sauté over medium heat about 15 minutes or until browned; add a few tablespoons of stock if the onions begin to stick. Stir in bell peppers and sauté for 3 minutes. Stir in garlic, sweet paprika and hot paprika, and sauté for 1 minute. Add tomatoes and remaining stock and bring to a boil.

Return turkey to pan, along with the juices that have collected on the plate. Cover and cook over low heat, turning once, for about 40 minutes or until done. Remove turkey once more to a plate. Boil sauce to thicken it (3-4 minutes). Add spices to taste, especially hot paprika. Cut turkey into thin slices and serve with sauce.

Makes 4 servings.

Herb-seasoned Turkey Patties

This quick and easy yet satisfying dinner is great for nights on the run.

1 pound ground turkey
¼ cup chopped onion
1 teaspoon salt
½ teaspoon ground black pepper
½ teaspoon each dried marjoram, basil and sage leaves
1 egg
4 tablespoons butter
thinly sliced cucumber and lemon for garnish

Combine turkey with onion, salt, black pepper, marjoram, basil, sage and egg. Shape into 4 large patties. Heat butter in heavy skillet and add turkey patties. Sauté slowly over medium low heat (about 10 minutes on each side), or until cooked through. Remove to a heated platter. Top each patty with lemon and cucumber slices.

Makes 4 servings.

Turkey Breast in Lemon Sauce

Lemon plays a key role in this dish's preparation. It keeps the meat moist during roasting, and it adds a piquant nuance to the spicy sauce.

1½ pounds turkey breast, boned, skin on
salt and pepper
2 tablespoons melted butter
6 ounces of fresh lemon juice
2 teaspoon dry mustard
1 teaspoon each paprika and ginger
1 teaspoon salt
lemon wedges and lettuce leaves for garnish

Lightly sprinkle turkey breast with salt and pepper. Place into shallow roasting pan. Mix butter and lemon juice and pour evenly over turkey. Cover bird loosely with foil, to allow air circulation.

Bake at 350 degrees for 1½ hours or until turkey is cooked though. Remove turkey from pan. Pour juices into small skillet and bring to a boil. Whisk in mustard, paprika, ginger and salt. Heat until sauce thickens.

Glaze meat with a few tablespoonfuls of sauce, spooning remaining sauce around turkey. Thinly slice turkey and serve with sauce on the side. Garnish with lemon wedges and lettuce leaves.

Makes 4 servings.

Curried Turkey Tenderloins

This recipe calls for 1-2 hours of marinating prior to grilling. The tenderloins are flavored with lime, curry, garlic, cumin and cinnamon.

1 pound turkey tenderloins
¼ cup olive oil
3 tablespoons lime juice
1 tablespoon dried minced onion
2 teaspoons curry powder
½ teaspoon grated lime rind
½ teaspoon garlic powder
¼ teaspoon salt
¼ teaspoon ground cumin
¼ teaspoon ground cinnamon
¼ teaspoon pepper

Butterfly tenderloins by cutting each tenderloin lengthwise, taking care not to cut all the way through. Between two sheets of wax paper, gently flatten the butterflied tenderloin using the smooth side of a meat tenderizer. In a sealable plastic bag, combine oil, juice, onion, curry, lime rind, garlic powder, salt, cumin, cinnamon, pepper and tenderloins. Close bag and refrigerate 1-2 hours. On an outdoor grill, cook tenderloins 5-6 minutes per side or until done.

Makes 4 servings.

Roast Turkey with Rosemary

1 whole turkey (10 to 12 pounds)
6 to 8 cloves garlic
2 large lemons, halved
2 teaspoons dried rosemary, crushed
1 teaspoon rubbed sage
½ stick butter, melted

Cut 6 to 8 small slits in turkey skin. Insert garlic between the skin and the meat. Squeeze 2 lemon halves inside the turkey and leave them inside. Brush melted butter over outside of the turkey and inside slits. Squeeze remaining lemon over the outside of the turkey. Sprinkle with rosemary and sage. Place on a rack in roasting pan. Bake, uncovered, at 325 degrees for 1 hour. Baste with pan juices. Cover and bake for 2½ to 3½ hours longer until meat thermometer reads 185 degrees, basting every ½ hour with pan juices.

Turkey Meat Loaf

3 pounds ground turkey
2 tablespoons chili powder
3 eggs
3 gloves garlic, minced
3 tablespoons parsley, chopped
1 tablespoon tomato juice
salt and pepper to taste

Preheat oven to 375 degrees. In a large bowl, thoroughly mix all ingredients. Place turkey mixture into oiled loaf pan and bake for 45 minutes to 1 hour. Salt and pepper to taste.

Baked Cornish Game Hens

Cornish game hens stuffed with vegetables and then roasted makes an excellent meal for four.

2 Cornish game hens
½ cup melted butter
½ onion, chopped
½ stalk celery, chopped
¼ green bell pepper, chopped
½ cup sliced black olives
2 cloves garlic, minced
1 tablespoon dried basil
1 teaspoon dried oregano
1 tablespoon chopped fresh parsley
¼ cup melted butter

Preheat oven to 325 degrees. In a small bowl, combine vegetables and herbs and spices with half a cup of melted butter. Season hens inside and out with salt and pepper to taste, then stuff with equal amounts of the vegetable mixture. Place birds in a 9x13 inch baking dish, breast side up. Drizzle with ¼ cup melted butter. Cover dish and bake for 1½ hours. Finally, remove cover and brown at 500 degrees.

Makes 4 servings.

SEAFOOD

Seafood

Interestingly, it has now been scientifically documented that oils found in cold water fish have tremendous benefit to our blood system, including the heart! Combine that fact with our garlic dill fish or smoked haddock and you've got a healthy recipe that tastes great! From snapper to cod, we've covered a lot of bases to allow fish back into your diet and have it benefit you as well!

Red Snapper in Tomato Sauce

two 6- to 8-ounce red snapper fillets
¼ cup chopped green onions
2 tablespoons butter, melted
2 large tomatoes, seeded and chopped
1 tablespoon chopped fresh cilantro
3 tablespoons fresh lime juice
2 tablespoons canned chopped green chiles
¼ teaspoon salt
1/8 teaspoon garlic powder
pinch of pepper
lime wedges

In a large skillet, fry green onions in butter until tender, stirring constantly. Stir in tomatoes and the following 6 ingredients. Bring to a boil. Reduce heat and simmer for 10 minutes.

Lay fish into skillet, spooning tomato mixture evenly over the fillets. Bring to a boil. Cover, reduce heat and simmer for 10 minutes or until fish flakes easily when tested with a fork. Serve with lime wedges.

Makes 2 servings.

Lemon-Basil Grilled Tuna

Grilled over hot coals, fresh tuna steaks take on a ranch-like character.

6 tuna steaks (1½ inches thick and about 1½ pounds worth)
1 large lemon
1 teaspoon basil
¼ cup olive oil
1 teaspoon salt
½ teaspoon pepper

Place tuna steaks in an 11x7 inch baking dish. Grate lemon rind, and squeeze juice from lemon into a bowl. Mix in remaining 4 ingredients and pour over steaks. Cover and marinate in refrigerator 1½ hours, turning steaks once.

Coat grill rack with olive oil and place on grill over medium-hot coals (350-400 degrees). Lay steaks out on rack, and grill (covered with grill lid) 5 minutes on each side or until fish flakes easily when tested with a fork.

Makes 6 servings.

Ceviche of Sea Bass

3 pounds fresh sea bass fillets
4 cups diced tomatoes
4 cups diced cucumbers
3 cups diced red onions
1 cup chopped cilantro
½ cup chopped fresh parsley
juice of 6 lemons
salt and pepper to taste

Cut fillets into half-inch-square pieces and place them in a bowl. Mix in all the remaining ingredients, reserving some of the lemon juice for adjusting the dish's flavor later. Add just enough water to cover everything. Cover and marinate in the refrigerator for at least 3 hours.

Remove the ceviche from the refrigerator just before serving. Add reserved lemon juice, plus salt and pepper, to taste. Serve ceviche in individual bowls.

Makes 12 servings.

Fennel-fried Fish

1¼ pounds thick fish fillets (grouper works well)
1 tablespoon olive oil
3 tablespoons fennel seed
2 tablespoons water

Cut fish crosswise into ½-inch thick slices and set aside. Pour oil into a skillet large enough to hold fish pieces in one layer. Add fennel seed and sauté for a few seconds. Add fish and fry for about 2 minutes over medium heat. Add a tablespoon of water and cover skillet. Two minutes later, add a second tablespoon of water and replace the cover. Steam fish until it is cooked through. Serve immediately.

Makes 4 servings.

Spicy Salmon with Asparagus

This recipe is as delicious as it is colorful, fresh and light.

one 1¼-pound salmon fillet, about 1 inch thick
1 tablespoon and ½ teaspoon strained fresh lemon juice
1 tablespoon and 1 teaspoon extra-virgin olive oil
1 teaspoon ground cumin
1 teaspoon ground coriander
½ teaspoon paprika
½ teaspoon dried thyme
salt and fresh-ground black pepper to taste
cayenne pepper to taste
1 pound medium-width asparagus

Preheat oven to 450 degrees. Lay salmon into a heavy roasting pan. Sprinkle fish with 1 tablespoon lemon juice and 1 tablespoon oil. Rub into fish. Sprinkle fish with cumin, coriander, paprika and thyme. Rub lightly. Finally, sprinkle salmon evenly with salt, pepper and cayenne. Roast uncovered about 12 minutes, or until the flesh just flakes and has changed color at its thickest part.

Peel and trim the asparagus spears and cut them into 3 pieces each. Boil in a saucepan of salted water about 3 minutes, or until crisp-tender. Drain and toss with ½ teaspoon lemon juice, 1 teaspoon olive oil, salt and pepper.

Arrange salmon on a platter and spoon asparagus around it. Serve hot.

Makes 4 servings.

Cod with Tomato-Basil Salsa

For the salsa, use plum tomatoes — their thin skins and small number of seeds make peeling and straining unnecessary.

four 6-ounce cod fillets (preferably Pacific)
salt and fresh-ground black pepper to taste
1 clove garlic
8 ounces Italian plum tomatoes (about 2)
½ cup packed basil leaves
½ teaspoon coarse salt
2 tablespoons freshly squeezed lime juice
pinch of cayenne pepper

Fish

Preheat oven to 450 degrees. Line a baking dish with foil. Season both sides of fillets with salt and pepper, lay in baking pan and bake for about 12 minutes, or until cooked through.

Salsa

Peel and smash garlic clove. Core and cut each tomato into 8 chunks. In a food processor, pulse garlic, tomatoes, basil, salt, lime juice and cayenne pepper to a chunky purée.

Serve ¼ cup salsa atop each fillet.

Makes 4 servings.

Blackened Fish

Use smaller amounts of spices and herbs for a milder version.

1 teaspoon paprika
¼ teaspoon white pepper
1 ¼ pounds skinned fish fillets
½ teaspoon freshly ground black pepper
¼ teaspoon cayenne
½ teaspoon oregano
½ teaspoon thyme
½ teaspoon basil
½ teaspoon salt (optional)

Preheat broiler. Combine seasonings on a plate. Roll each fillet to coat, rubbing mix into both sides. Broil fillets until cooked through (5-20 minutes, depending on thickness of fish).

Makes 4 servings.

Garlic Dill Fish

1 ½ pounds fish fillets (flounder, sole, turbot, etc.)
1 teaspoon dill weed
1 clove garlic, minced
¼ cup fresh lime juice
salt and fresh-ground black pepper to taste

Preheat oven to 350 degrees. Squeeze lime juice over fillets, marinating for at least 30 minutes in refrigerator.

Lay fillets in a shallow baking pan greased with butter. Sprinkle with dill, garlic, salt, and pepper. Bake for 5-10 minutes or until fish flakes easily.

Makes 6 servings.

Sea Bass with Basil & Tomato

This dish is great served hot or cold. The saffron-oil based sauce can be prepared in advance and either refrigerated or frozen.

½ teaspoon saffron threads
3 tablespoons extra-virgin olive oil
1 medium onion, chopped
½ cup diced red bell pepper
1½ pounds ripe tomatoes, peeled, seeded, and puréed
(or 42 ounces of canned plum tomatoes, drained and puréed)
salt and freshly ground pepper to taste
1½ to 1¾ pounds of sea bass fillets, about 1 inch thick
3 tablespoons chopped fresh basil or Italian parsley

Pour olive oil into a cup. Slightly crush saffron with your fingers and submerge in oil for about 20 minutes. Transfer "saffron oil" to a large sauté pan or skillet and cook briefly over low heat. Add onion and bell pepper and sauté over medium-low heat about 5 minutes or until onion begins to turn golden. Add tomatoes, salt and pepper and cook over medium-high heat, stirring often, for 8 to 10 minutes or until the mixture thickens.

Add sea bass in one layer. Sprinkle with salt and pepper, cover and cook over medium-low heat for about 10 minutes, spooning sauce over fish from time to time. The thickest part of fish should turn opaque inside — check this with a sharp knife. Taste sauce and adjust seasoning. Stir 2 tablespoons basil gently into sauce. Serve hot or cold, sprinkled with the remaining basil.

Makes 4 main courses, or about 6 fish-course servings.

Halibut in Pepper Sauce

This recipe can be prepared a day in advance and refrigerated. In fact, the flavor of the fish deepens as it chills. Haddock, cod or sea bass may be substituted for the halibut.

2 pounds of halibut fillets, about 1 inch thick
2 tablespoons olive oil
1 medium onion, halved and sliced thin
1 pound green bell peppers (or green, red and yellow)
2 teaspoons paprika
1 pound ripe tomatoes, peeled, seeded, and diced
(or one 28-ounce can of diced tomatoes, drained)
salt and fresh-ground pepper to taste
pinch of hot paprika or cayenne pepper (optional)

Sauce

In medium-sized skillet, heat oil and add onion, sautéing over medium-low heat for 5 minutes or until onion begins to turn golden. Cut peppers into strips half an inch wide and 2 inches long. Combine them with the onions and sauté, stirring occasionally, for 15 minutes. Add paprika and sauté another minute, stirring constantly. Finally, add tomatoes, salt and pepper. Cover and simmer, stirring occasionally, for about 15 minutes or until peppers are tender and mixture thickens. Adjust seasoning, adding hot paprika to taste. *(If not serving immediately, refrigerate pepper sauce in a covered container.)*

Fish

Preheat oven to 425 degrees. Lightly oil a shallow baking dish large enough to hold fish in a single layer. Reheat pepper sauce if necessary. Spread half of sauce in dish. Arrange halibut fillets on top, in a single layer, and cover with remaining sauce. Bake uncovered for about 15 minutes or until thickest part of fish becomes opaque inside; check with a sharp knife. Serve hot or chilled.

Makes 6 main-course or 8-10 appetizer servings.

Garlic & Rosemary Broiled Fish

Use savory fish such as salmon, cod and halibut — they tend to stand up better to the robust combination of rosemary and garlic.

1 teaspoon minced fresh rosemary (1/4 teaspoon if dried)
1 medium clove garlic minced
1/2 teaspoon paprika
cayenne pepper to taste
1-2 tablespoons extra-virgin olive oil
salt and fresh-ground pepper to taste
1 to 4 pounds sea bass fillets or steaks, about 1 inch thick
lemon wedges

Preheat broiler with rack positioned about 4 inches from heat source. Sprinkle fish lightly with salt. In a small bowl, combine rosemary, garlic, paprika, cayenne and oil. Spoon half of the mixture over one side of fish, rubbing it in with your fingers. Lay fish on broiler rack with rubbed side up and broil for 5 minutes. Flip, sprinkle reverse side with salt and rub with remaining garlic mixture. Broil 4 to 5 more minutes, or until thickest part of fish becomes opaque inside; check with a sharp knife. Garnish with lemon wedges and serve hot.

Makes 4 servings.

Baked Salmon Fillet

This light dish features salmon flavored with a dry rub of thyme, oregano and cumin. Flash broiling after baking gives it a tasty crust.

one 1¼- to 1½-pound salmon fillet, about 1 inch thick
½ teaspoon dried thyme
½ teaspoon dried oregano
½ teaspoon ground cumin
½ teaspoon paprika
salt and fresh-ground pepper to taste
lemon wedges

Preheat oven to 450 degrees. Place fish on a heavy roasting pan lined with foil. Combine thyme, oregano, cumin and paprika and sprinkle evenly over fish. Refrigerate 10-15 minutes. Dust fish evenly with salt and pepper.

Roast fish in oven about 10 minutes, or until the thickest part of the fish is pink inside; check with a sharp knife. Finally, broil fish for 30 to 60 seconds, to lightly brown the surface. Garnish with lemon wedges and serve.

Makes 4 servings.

Lemony Trout with Asparagus

This quick and easy dish features a sauce of fresh lemon juice, olive oil and Italian parsley. Salmon fillets can be substituted for the trout.

1 pound thin asparagus, thick bases removed
1¼ to 1½ pounds of red trout fillet, 1-inch thick
2 tablespoons strained fresh lemon juice

1 to 2 tablespoons olive oil
salt and fresh-ground pepper to taste
1 green onion, chopped
¼ cup chopped fresh Italian parsley
cayenne pepper to taste
lemon wedges
2 tablespoons water

Preheat oven to 375 degrees. Cut each asparagus spear into 3 pieces, rinse and boil in a saucepan for 2 minutes. Drain and rinse with cold water. Lightly oil a baking dish into which fish and asparagus can be placed in one layer. Lay fish in dish and sprinkle with 1 tablespoon lemon juice, 1 teaspoon olive oil, salt, pepper, and green onion. Add 2 tablespoons water. Bake uncovered for 7 minutes.

Add asparagus to baking dish around fish. Cover lightly with foil and bake another 5 minutes, or until asparagus is tender and the thickest part of the fish is opaque inside; check with a sharp knife. Cover fish to keep it warm.

In a small bowl, blend remaining lemon juice, olive oil and parsley with a whisk. Season this with salt, pepper, and cayenne. Spoon over fish and garnish with lemon wedges.

Makes 4 servings.

Salmon in Walnut Sauce

Accompanied by flash-cooked broccoli florets, this tasty salmon in a rich sauce makes a terrific and easy entrée for any festive occasion.

Sauce

3 large clove garlic, peeled
1/3 cup sprigs fresh parsley
2/3 cup walnuts
salt and fresh-ground pepper to taste
2 tablespoons cold water
½ to 3/4 cup oil
cayenne pepper to taste

Finely chop garlic in a food processor. Add parsley sprigs and continue chopping. Add walnuts, salt, and pepper and process until walnuts are finely ground. Add water and purée to a smooth paste. Finally, with blades still turning, gradually pour in oil, stopping occasionally to scrape down sides and bottom of work bowl. Transfer mixture to a bowl, add cayenne and adjust seasoning to taste. Serve sauce at room temperature, stirring before serving.

Salmon

2 pounds salmon fillet, about 1 inch thick
2 tablespoons strained fresh lemon juice
2 teaspoons olive oil
2 teaspoons ground coriander
1 teaspoon dried oregano
salt and fresh-ground pepper to taste
lemon wedges

Preheat broiler. Sprinkle salmon with lemon juice and oil, rubbing this into fillet. Dust fish evenly with coriander, oregano, salt and pepper. Line broiler rack with foil if you like, or lightly brush rack with oil. Place fish on rack and broil for 4 minutes. Turn over and broil 4-5 minutes more, or until the thickest part of the fish is the palest of pinks inside; check with a sharp knife.

Cut fish into 6 portions and top with a dollop of sauce. Garnish with lemon wedges and parsley sprigs and serve.

Makes 6 servings.

Sea Scallops & Spinach

1 to 2 pounds fresh scallops, chopped
1 tablespoon minced garlic
1 whole onion, diced
1 to 2 cups fresh leaf spinach
1 cup diced tomatoes
1 teaspoon butter

In a fry pan over medium heat, sauté onions and garlic in butter until onions are just browned. Add scallops and continue cooking until fish is thoroughly cooked, stirring occasionally. Add leaf spinach and tomatoes. Continue cooking for 5-10 minutes, until spinach is cooked.

Makes 4-6 servings.

Trout with Paprika & Cilantro

This easy dish features trout spiced with garlic, cilantro and paprika. For a spicier meal, add minced jalapeño along with the garlic.

4 whole trout
3 tablespoons olive oil
2 teaspoons paprika
4 large cloves garlic, minced
¼ cup chopped fresh cilantro
salt and fresh-ground pepper to taste

In a small bowl, combine oil and paprika. Let stand at room temperature for at least an hour, preferably several, stirring occasionally. Add garlic and cilantro to "paprika oil" and mix well.

If trout still has fins, snip them with sturdy scissors and trim tails straight. Rinse fish inside and out, removing any scales, and pat dry.

Preheat oven to 400 degrees. Place trout on a large tray with skin side down. Sprinkle inside and out with salt and pepper. Spoon about half of the garlic mixture over trout. Fold each fish in half, reforming them. Place them on pieces of foil large enough to wrap them in. Spoon on remaining garlic mixture, lightly rubbing it in. Wrap each trout tightly in the foil. Lay wrapped trout into a roasting pan. Bake trout about 20 minutes or until a thin skewer inserted into thickest part of fish comes out hot to touch. Serve hot in foil packets.

Makes 4 servings.

Fillet of Fish Almondine

This simple dish is quite tasty.

¼ cup olive oil or butter
3 tablespoons slivered almonds
2 pounds fish fillets (snapper, cod)
1 tablespoons lemon juice
½ teaspoon garlic salt
¼ teaspoon pepper

Heat 2 tablespoons of oil in a large skillet. Add almonds and sauté for 2 to 3 minutes, stirring constantly until golden brown. Remove almonds and set aside. In remaining oil, fry fish 3-4 minutes on each side until it flakes when pierced with fork. Remove to warm platter. Combine pan drippings with lemon juice, salt, pepper and almonds and spoon over fish.

Makes 2 servings.

Makes 2 servings.

Smoked Haddock Paté

This dish qualifies as a convenience food in that it can be prepared ahead of time and needs little last-minute attention. Other fish such as smoked cod or salmon can be substituted for the haddock. If the fish you have in mind is especially salty, try using unsalted butter. Plan to chill the paté for at least 3 hours or overnight for best flavor. Serve it in a handsome crock and let your family help themselves.

½ pound smoked haddock
water
2 tablespoons lemon juice
½ teaspoon butter, melted
1/3 cup whipping cream
coarsely ground black pepper
chopped parsley and sliced, ripe, black olives for garnish

Place smoked fish in a small plan. Add enough water to cover, bring to a boil and reduce heat. Cover and simmer until fish flakes easily, 15-20 minutes. Let fish cool in cooking liquid. Drain and separate fish into flakes, discarding any bones.

Spoon fish, lemon juice, and thyme into a food processor or blender. Cover and blend until smooth. Add butter in a slow, steady stream, puréeing until mixture is smooth.

Whip cream until stiff. Fold in fish mixture until well combined. Add pepper to taste. Cover and refrigerate to blend flavors, several hours or overnight. Remove from refrigerator about 30 minutes before serving. Garnish with parsley and olive slices. Serve as a dip/spread with chunks and slices of raw vegetables.

Chilled Cod in Red Sauce

This dish is best served with a green salad.

6 fillets of cod (about 3 ounces each)
¼ cup olive oil
¼ cup fresh parsley, minced
8 ounces pimento, chopped
salt and pepper
one 28-ounce can tomato purée
3 tomatoes, chopped
2 carrots, sliced
2 strips celery, sliced
2 cloves garlic, minced
water
3 tablespoons fresh lemon juice
1 packet of powdered Stevia

In a large saucepan, combine parsley, pimento, salt, pepper, tomato purée and fresh tomatoes. Bring to a boil and add carrots, celery and garlic. Simmer until carrots are cooked, but still firm. Stir in a little water and the juice of 1 lemon.

Lay cod fillets into pan without stirring, basting fish with the juices. Add stevia. Cook fish until done, removing it from heat. Cool and then chill.

Makes 6 servings.

Baked Lemony Salmon

four 1½-pound salmon steaks
¼ cup butter, melted
1 teaspoon lemon-pepper seasoning
1 teaspoon garlic salt
1 teaspoon paprika
lemon wedges

Place steaks in an llx7 inch baking dish. Thoroughly combine butter, lemon-pepper seasoning, and garlic salt in a small bowl and pour over steaks. Sprinkle with paprika.

Baked uncovered at 500 degrees for 10 minutes or until fish flakes easily when tested with fork. Serve with lemon wedges.

Makes 4 servings.

Lettuce-wrapped Shrimp

½ pound shrimp, thawed and peeled
8 large lettuce leaves
½ cup "Tomato Salsa"
¼ cup minced peeled red onion
1 avocado, pitted, peeled and cubed
¼ teaspoon ground black pepper
2 limes, cut into wedges

Preheat oven to 350 degrees. Bring a medium saucepan of salted water to a boil. Add shrimp and gently poach until just pink, about 2 minutes; drain and cool. Divide salsa evenly between lettuce leaves. Top with shrimp, onion and avocado; season with pepper. Serve immediately with lime wedges.

pepper. Serve immediately with lime wedges.

Lemon-Tarragon Lobster

2 live lobsters, each about ½ pound
1 tablespoon chopped fresh tarragon
¼ cup butter
2 tablespoons fresh lemon juice
1½ teaspoons grated lemon peel
2 tablespoons chives, chopped
salt and pepper

Stir butter, lemon juice and lemon peel in a saucepan over low heat, until butter melts. Mix in chives and tarragon and season with salt and pepper.

Meanwhile, bring large pot of water to boil. Plunge lobsters head-first into water. Cover pot and boil for 2 minutes. Transfer lobsters to work surface.

Using heavy knife or cleaver, split the lobsters in half lengthwise. Scoop out and discard gray intestinal tract, gills and sand sac from head. Leave any red roe or green tomalley intact, if desired. Crack claws.

Brush cut sides of lobsters with 1 tablespoon butter sauce. Bake at 450 degrees, turning once, until lobster meat is just opaque but

Lobster in White Sauce

1½ pounds uncooked lobster tails
1 bunch spinach
1 medium onion
4 large garlic cloves
1 small fresh serrano chile
1 inch piece fresh gingerroot
½ teaspoon mustard seeds
2 tablespoons olive oil
1 cup plain yogurt
1 teaspoon salt

With a cleaver or a large knife, halve lobster tails lengthwise. Discard shells and de-vein tails. Cut meat into bite-size pieces.

Discard stems from spinach and chop enough spinach to measure 2 cups. Chop onion and mince garlic and serrano. Peel and mince gingerroot. Grind mustard seeds.

In a 10- to 12-inch, heavy skillet, heat oil over medium heat. Add onion, garlic, serrano, gingerroot and mustard seeds, stirring until onion begins to brown. Stir in spinach and cook until it begins to wilt, or about 30 seconds.

Gradually add yogurt, stirring until combined well, and stir in lobster and salt. Simmer mixture gently until lobster is just cooked through, or 5 to 6 minutes.

Lobster-stuffed Eggs

¼ pound cooked lobster meat or the meat of 1 cooked king crab leg, chopped fine (about ½ cup)
2 radishes, chopped fine
2 scallion, chopped fine
2 celery stalks, chopped fine
1 tablespoon minced parsley
2 tablespoons Texas mayonnaise
2 teaspoons lemon juice
1/8 teaspoon tomato juice
3 hard-boiled eggs
½ cup finely shredded romaine for garnish
½ cup finely shredded cabbage for garnish
salt and pepper

In a bowl, combine the lobster, radishes, scallion, celery, parsley, mayonnaise, lemon juice, tomato juice, salt and pepper to taste. Halve the eggs crosswise and remove the yolks. Chop 1 of the yolks, reserving the other 2 for another use, and stir it into the lobster salad.

Divide the romaine and the cabbage between 2 salad plates, forming nests. Fill egg whites with the lobster mixture and arrange over salad leaves.

Parchment-Baked Halibut

1 cup coarsely chopped onions
2 tablespoons olive oil
2 cups thickly sliced green apples (about 2 medium)
½ teaspoon crushed thyme
½ teaspoon crushed rosemary
1/8 teaspoon salt
1/8 teaspoon pepper
4 (4-6 ounces each) North Pacific halibut steaks, thawed
2 teaspoons lemon juice
2 teaspoons minced parsley

Sauté onions in olive oil over medium-high heat about 5 minutes, or until onions are browned. Remove from heat and stir in apples, thyme, oregano, rosemary, salt and pepper. Set aside.

Cut four pieces of parchment paper and spray with nonstick spray. Place halibut steaks next to the fold on sprayed side of parchment paper. Sprinkle ½ teaspoon each lemon juice and minced parsley over halibut, and season to taste with salt and pepper.

Fold other half of parchment paper over halibut. Seal edges with tightly creased overlapping folds. Place on baking sheet. Bake at 400 degrees for 10 minutes, or until packets are puffed and lightly browned. Remove from oven, cut paper around halibut and serve immediately. *Makes 4 servings*.

Mediterranean Baked Fish

1 pound cod fillets
2 medium zucchini, sliced
4 medium tomatoes, diced

¼ cup olive oil
1 tablespoon lemon juice
½ teaspoon garlic
¼ teaspoon oregano
1 lemon, cut into 4 wedges

Preheat oven to 400 degrees. Mix zucchini and tomatoes in baking dish; top with cod fillets. Spoon olive oil evenly over fish. Sprinkle fish with lemon juice, garlic, and oregano. Bake for 15 minutes. Flip fillets. Bake an additional 10 to 12 minutes or until fish flakes evenly with fork. Serve with lemon wedges.

Shrimp Scampi

1 pound shrimp, cleaned and shelled
3 tablespoons butter
2½ tablespoons olive oil
½ tablespoon of fresh grapefruit juice
4 large cloves garlic
1 teaspoon parsley, chopped
juice of ½ lemon
pinch of red pepper flakes
salt and pepper to taste

Heat the butter and oil in a skillet over medium-hot heat until the foam subsides. Add the garlic, parsley, lemon juice, grapefruit juice, pepper flakes, salt and pepper. Bring to a boil, lower heat, and simmer for 3 minutes. Add shrimp and cook, stirring frequently, for 5 to 7 minutes until shrimp are pink. Remove from heat. Serve shrimp covered in sauce.

Blackened Catfish

2 teaspoons paprika
½ teaspoon oregano
½ teaspoon thyme
¼ teaspoon cayenne pepper (or to taste)
½ teaspoon salt
¼ teaspoons freshly ground black pepper
2 catfish fillets (about 1 pound)
1 large clove garlic, sliced thin
1 tablespoon olive oil
1 tablespoon butter
lemon wedges as an accompaniment

In a small bowl, combine paprika, oregano, thyme, cayenne, salt and black pepper. Pat the catfish dry and sprinkle the spice mixture on both sides of the fillet, coating them well.

In a large skillet, sauté the garlic in the oil over moderately high heat, stirring, until it is golden brown and discard the garlic. Add the butter, heat it until the foam subsides and sauté the catfish for 4 to 5 minutes on each side, or until it is cooked through.

Transfer the catfish fillets with a spatula to 2 plates and serve them with the lemon wedges.

Cajun Catfish

2 tablespoons butter
2 tablespoons olive oil
4 catfish fillets
1 onion
1 tablespoon garlic powder
1 tablespoon plus ½ teaspoon black pepper
1 tablespoon paprika
1 ½ teaspoon cayenne pepper
1 teaspoon salt

Combine all ingredients except for the catfish in a cast-iron skillet over high heat until hot but not smoking. Simmer until onion is limp and translucent. Pat fish dry.

Place fish in hot skillet and cook until it is opaque on the bottom, approximately 5 minutes. Turn fish carefully. Cook until the fish flakes easily, about 3 minutes. Serve with "Almost Tartar Sauce."

Spinach-wrapped Shrimps

3 tomatoes, peeled
¼ teaspoon freshly ground pepper
1¼ teaspoon sea salt
½ tablespoon grapefruit juice
5 quarts water
16 medium raw shrimp, in the shell (about 12 ounces total)
1 teaspoon butter
16 large spinach leaves (about 8 ounces total), stems removed

Process tomatoes with a food processor until smooth. Add ¼ teaspoon sea salt, pepper, and grapefruit juice and process a few seconds more. Reserve purée.

Bring the water and remaining sea salt to a boil. Add the shrimp and cook until the water begins to boil again and the shrimp are bright pink. Drain and peel the shrimp. Discard the shells.

Melt the butter and cook the spinach, stirring, for about 1 minute. Remove from pan and spread on paper towels.

Wrap one leaf around the wide part of each shrimp, leaving the tail end exposed. Divide the tomato purée evenly among 4 plates. Arrange 4 shrimp on each plate.

Crab Legs with Dipping Sauce

3 pounds or more of crab legs
4 tablespoons butter, melted
2 teaspoons lemon juice
½ teaspoon salt
½ teaspoon pepper

Fill a large sauté or fry pan with water to ½-inch depth; add crab legs and bring to a boil. Reduce heat, cover and simmer for 4 minutes. While crab legs simmer, combine all other ingredients and heat. Drain crab legs and serve with dipping sauce.

Bacon-wrapped Shrimps

20 strips of bacon
2 bunches basil
40 medium shrimp, peeled (tails on)
1/8 teaspoon salt
1/8 teaspoon black pepper
4 lemons, cut into wedges

Preheat broiler. Cut bacon strips in half width-wise. On a large cutting board lay bacon strips flat. Place basil leaf in the middle of each piece of bacon. Place a shrimp on top of the basil with the tail at a right angle to the bacon strip. Wrap the bacon around the shrimp and place down on a broiling pan. Secure with a toothpick if desired. Sprinkle with salt and pepper.

Broil 4 to 5 inches from heat source for 3 minutes. Turn and broil another 3 minutes, until shrimps are pink and curled and bacon is crisp. Squeeze lemon juice over the cooked shrimp just before serving.

Saucy Snapper & Bay Shrimp

4 tablespoons olive oil
2 celery stalks, chopped
1 medium onion, chopped
½ large green bell pepper, chopped
2 garlic cloves, chopped
1 teaspoon fennel seeds
¼ teaspoons dried crushed red pepper
2 chopped tomatoes
1/8 cup apple cider vinegar
2 tablespoons tomato juice (may use V8 juice)
4 6-ounce red snapper fillets
¼ cooked bay shrimp
salt and pepper

Heat 2 tablespoons of oil in a heavy, large saucepan over medium heat. Add celery, onion, green pepper, garlic, fennel seeds and crushed red pepper and sauté until vegetables are soft but not brown, about 9 minutes.

Mix in tomatoes, apple cider vinegar and tomato juice; simmer until sauce thickens, breaking up tomatoes with the back of the spoon, about 10 minutes.

Heat the remaining 2 tablespoons of oil in a heavy, large nonstick skillet over medium-high heat. Season snapper with salt and pepper and add to skillet. Sauté until brown, or about 2 minutes per side.

Pour sauce over snapper and top with shrimp. Simmer until fish is just cooked through, or about 10 minutes.

Crab Bisque

2½ cups water
2½ cups clam juice
¼ cup apple cider vinegar
1 medium onion, diced
2 stalks celery, diced
2 cloves garlic, peeled, whole
½ pound crab meat
½ teaspoon dill
1 cup heavy whipping cream
1 tablespoon tomato juice (may use V8 juice)
sea salt and pepper to taste

Combine the water, clam juice, apple cider vinegar, onion, celery, and garlic in a large soup pot; slowly bring to a boil. Reduce the heat and simmer for 30 minutes. Strain and return the liquid to the pot. Whisk in the cream and tomato juice. Add the remaining ingredients. Simmer for 25 minutes. Serve warm.

Lemon Pepper Catfish

½ to 1 pound catfish fillets
3 tablespoons butter
½ teaspoon pepper
¼ cup lemon juice
1/8 teaspoon parsley, chopped

Thaw fillets. In a large skillet, melt butter and add pepper and lemon juice. Add catfish. Cook on medium-high heat turning occasionally. Sprinkle with parsley while cooking. Cook until flaky. Serve in sauce.

Mexican Snapper

1 tablespoon olive oil
½ cup chopped onion
4 diced green chilies
4 tablespoons chopped fresh cilantro
3 large garlic cloves, chopped
2 large tomatoes, diced
1¼ pounds red snapper fillets
lime wedges

Heat oil in large skillet, over medium-high heat. Spoon in onion and sauté for 3 minutes. Add green chilies, 2 tablespoons chopped cilantro and garlic. Sauté for 2 minutes and then mix in tomatoes.

Place fish on top of sauce in pan and bring to a simmer. Cover, reduce heat to medium-low and continue to simmer until fish is just opaque in center, or about 8-9 minutes. Transfer fish to platter.

Simmer sauce to thicken it slightly and spoon over fish. Sprinkle with remaining 2 tablespoons of cilantro, frame with lime wedges and serve.

JUICES
&
OTHER
BEVERAGES

Juices & Other Beverages

Fresh vegetable juices are low in sugar and contain a broad array of vitamins, minerals and enzymes. Our bodies assimilate the nutrients from juices with comparatively little effort by our digestive systems. So, they carry health benefits that far outweigh the energy required to make, drink and digest them.

Juices are excellent for you even if you've got energy to spare, and especially if you suffer from fatigue. Adding juices to a diet poor in nutrition is less effective than using them to augment a balanced food regimen. Beyond their health aspect, fresh juices are simply great with breakfast, as an afternoon snack or simply to enjoy after a long day.

Carrot Juice

7 to 8 medium carrots

Thoroughly wash the carrots and trim off both ends, which tend to make juice slightly bitter. Run the carrots though your juicer. Pour in a glass and enjoy!

Makes 1 glass.

Celery-Carrot Juice

2 celery stalks, ends trimmed and leaves removed
6 medium-sized carrots, ends trimmed

Wash the vegetables well and run them through juicer. *Makes 1 glass.*

Veggie Cocktail Juice

This drink is great as a before-dinner cocktail. Drink slowly, immediately after making it.

6 to 7 medium-sized carrots, ends trimmed
4-5 celery stalks, ends trimmed
3 medium-sized tomatoes, quartered
1 medium-sized green or red bell pepper
a handful of spinach, parsley, or lettuce
1 tiny wedge of beet — about half of a small beet (optional)
dash of lemon

Wash all the vegetables thoroughly. Quarter the pepper, remove and discard its seeds. Run vegetables through juicer. Stir juice well and remove any foam from the top. Spice with a dash of lemon and serve with a carrot or celery swizzle stick.

Makes 3 servings.

Green Juice

½ cup asparagus
4 medium carrots
1 radish
2 handful spinach
4 collard leaves
3 stalks celery
1 cup watercress
1 scallion

Wash ingredients thoroughly. Combine, juice and serve.

Makes 1 glass.

Cabbage Juice

¼ head cabbage
2 stalks celery
1 cup fennel

Wash ingredients thoroughly. Combine, juice and serve.
Makes 1 glass.

Pepper Juice

1 large green pepper and 1 large red pepper, stems removed
3 celery stalks
1/3 medium cucumber
5 lettuce leaves

Wash ingredients thoroughly. Combine, juice and serve.
Makes 1 glass.

Eight Veggie Juice

¼ medium-sized cucumber
½ medium-sized tomato
1 medium-sized carrot
1 stalk celery
1 handful spinach
½ medium-sized red pepper
½ cup cabbage
1 scallion

Wash ingredients thoroughly. Combine, juice and serve.
Makes 1 glass.

Red Juice

3 radishes
½ medium-sized beet
¼ cup radish sprouts
½ medium-sized sweet red pepper
½ medium-sized cucumber

Wash ingredients thoroughly. Combine, juice and serve.
Makes 1 glass.

Popeye's Favorite Juice

5 handfuls spinach
2 medium-sized carrots
1 medium-sized cucumber

Wash ingredients thoroughly. Combine, juice and serve.
Makes 1 glass.

Whatever Goes Juice

3 medium-sized parsnips
5 leaves kale
1 cup artichoke hearts
1 cup cabbage
5 leaves lettuce
3 stalks celery
3 handfuls spinach
1 scallion

Wash ingredients thoroughly. Combine, juice and serve.
Makes 1 glass.

Ginger Tea

Look for knobs of fresh ginger in the produce section of your grocery store. Peel off the brown skins and grate the fibrous pulp to make this surprisingly spicy tea. The drink is best served over ice.

2 quarts water
1/3 to ½ cup grated fresh ginger
1/3 cup lemon juice
4 regular-size green tea bags
10 drops Stevia (liquid)

Combine first 4 ingredients in a Dutch oven; bring to a boil. Reduce heat and simmer for 5 minutes, stirring occasionally. Remove from heat.

Add tea bags and cover and steep 5 minutes, remove tea bags and stir-in stevia drops; pour tea through a wire-mesh strainer into a pitcher. Serve over ice.

Green Apple Lemonade

3 large Granny Smith apples, peeled and cored
juice of two large lemons
1 teaspoon Stevia sweetener
1 cup cold water
ice cubes

Use a juicer to extract the juice from the apples. Combine this with the other ingredients in a small pitcher. Mix well and pour into two tall glasses.

Frothy Lemonade

½ cup lemon juice
3 tablespoons honey
1 cup cold water
2 to 3 cups ice cubes
12 fresh mint leaves

Combine lemon juice, honey, water and ice cubes in blender. Blend on high until mixture is light and frothy and ice cubes are finely crushed. Place additional ice cubes and mint leaves in 12-ounce glasses. Pour in lemonade and serve immediately.

Makes 4 servings.

Mint-Strawberry Lemonade

2 quarts water
2 mint tea bags
8 sprigs fresh mint, plus 4 additional for garnish
12 strawberries
Juice of 2 lemons (approximately ¼ cup)
5 drops of Stevia, or to taste

Combine tea bags and mint leaves in a large bowl or pitcher. Pour in 2 quarts of boiling water and steep for 10 minutes.

Purée strawberries, lemon juice and stevia with a hand blender. Remove sprigs and tea bags from steeping solution and discard. Stir in strawberry-lemon mixture and mix well. Chill thoroughly before serving. When ready to serve, pour into individual glasses and garnish with additional mint sprigs.

Makes 4-6 glasses.

Green Apple Spritzer

1 cup fresh green apple juice (freshly juiced)
ice cubes
½ cup mineral water
dash of lime juice
slice of lime, for garnish

Pour apple juice over ice cubes. Add mineral water and lime juice and garnish with a slice of lime.

Makes 1 glass.

Almond Milk

For a whiter and smoother milk, first blanch the almonds. This recipe is easily doubled or tripled. It's great as a drink by itself, in shakes or smoothies, or as a base for soups and sauces.

½ cup raw almonds
2 cups purified water
pinch of pure Stevia powder (optional)

To blanch the almonds, place them in small sauce pan and cover them with water. Bring to a boil and drain. Carefully slip off their skins and dry well.

Place almonds in a blender and grind to fine powder. Add a cup of water and Stevia (if using) and blend 1 to 2 minutes. Continue blending and slowly add another cup of water. Blend 2 minutes. Pour liquid into an airtight, glass container. Keeps in refrigerator for 3-4 days.

Makes 2 cups.

Strawberry Milk

This drink is great for kids.

1 cup almond milk (recipe on pg. 247)
6 ripe strawberries
pinch of Stevia powder

Combine milk and strawberries in blender. Add sweetener if using, blend and serve.

Makes 1 glass.

Hot Ginger Tea

This tea counts as an excellent remedy for upset stomach. Sip it hot and enjoy both its warmth and its settling affect.

one 2-inch knob of ginger, finely chopped or grated
2 cups water

Combine ginger and water in a saucepan and boil for 10 minutes. Strain and drink immediately.

Serves 1.

Peppermint-Cinnamon Tea

1 peppermint tea bag
2 teaspoons lemon juice
1 cinnamon stick
1 cup boiling water
Stevia to taste

Place tea bag, lemon juice, and cinnamon stick in a mug. Add boiling water and steep for 2 to 3 minutes. Stir and add stevia to taste. Drink this one slowly.

Serves 1.

Pick-Me-Up Tea

This stimulating drink is virtually guaranteed to wake you up.

5 (1/8 inch thick) slices fresh ginger
5 cardamon pods
4 black peppercorns
3 whole cloves
1 cinnamon stick
2 cups water

Place all ingredients in a saucepan and bring to a boil. Remove from heat, allow to steep for a while to blend spices and then strain. Reheat to drink warm, or pour over ice and serve.

Serves 2.

Strawberry Smoothie

This drink is great on a hot day, or as an afternoon snack.

1 cup strawberry milk
1 cup fresh strawberry
½ almonds
ice

Combine all ingredients in blender. Blend for 15-30 seconds on high, pour into a glass and enjoy!

Makes 2 servings.

Desserts
&
Snacks

Desserts

A lot of people feel that the word dessert should be eliminated from any "healthy" eating philosophy. While we disagree, rethinking what passes for dessert is definitely in order. That's actually easier than it looks at first glance, because of the impact that the antifungal program is going to have upon your taste buds. Specifically, the concentrated sugars you once craved are actually going to taste *bad*. On the flip side, recipes such as the baked apples featured in this book will make your mouth water. These dishes will help you avoid becoming addicted to sugary sweets ever again, but still allow you to celebrate successfully staying on the diet.

Chunky Apple sauce

This dish is easy to make because you don't have to use a food mill, which can be tough to clean. Thinly slicing the apples shortens cooking time. This dish keeps for several days in the refrigerator.

2 to 4 tablespoons butter
3 pounds Granny Smith apples, peeled, cored and thinly sliced
2 teaspoons strained fresh lemon juice
grated rind of 1 lemon
Stevia to taste

Heat butter in a heavy stew pan or Dutch oven over medium heat. Add apples and sauté 2 minutes, turning pieces over several times until they are coated with butter. Stir in lemon juice and grated lemon rind. Cover tightly and cook over low heat, stirring often, for 25-30 minutes or until apples are very tender. As the apples cook, check the pan from time to time; if it looks dry, add 1 or 2 tablespoons of water.

Makes 8-10 servings.

Nutmeal Pie Crust

2 cups of walnuts (or other Initial-Phase friendly nuts)
3 tablespoons butter
2 teaspoons cinnamon
Stevia (optional)

Pour nuts into a grinder or food processor and make them very fine. Combine with remaining ingredients, pat into pie pan and bake at 350 degrees for 12 minutes.

Makes one 9 to 10 inch crust.

WAHOO! Cheesecake

This dish's name echoes what a lot of people say when they hear they can make and eat it, while still following the Initial Phase diet.

12 ounces cream cheese
2 eggs
1 tablespoon fresh lemon juice
½ cup heavy whipping cream
1 teaspoon of cinnamon
Stevia to taste (go sweeter than you might think)

Microwave cream cheese for 15 seconds to make it easier to mix without making lumps. In a large mixing bowl, combine cream cheese, lemon, stevia and 1 egg. Stir until well blended and as lump-free as possible. Add next egg and mix thoroughly. Fold in whipping cream until just mixed — do not over beat.

Pour into crust (see "Nutmeal Pie" crust recipe). To use a springform pan, increase the recipe by about half, or you will end up with a very flat cheesecake.

For a creamier cheesecake, bake using a water bath. Do so by placing the cheese-cake-filled pie pan in a larger pan — a roasting pan would work. Fill the larger pan with water until it reaches halfway up the sides of the cheesecake pan.

Bake at 350 degrees for 35-40 minutes, or until a toothpick inserted comes out clean. Remove from oven and cool to room temperature. Then chill for at least 2 hours. The top will crack while cooling. Serve with sliced strawberries or other Initial- Phase friendly fruits.

Makes one 9 to 10 inch pie.

Green Apples in Yogurt Sauce

This light snack is easy to make.

½ cup plain yogurt
½ cup sour cream
Stevia to taste
½ teaspoon ground cinnamon
4 Granny Smith apples, cored, peeled and sliced

Mix yogurt, sour cream, stevia, and cinnamon in a bowl. Pour over chilled apple slices and serve cold.

Makes 4 servings.

Spiced Baked Apples

6 large green apples
½ teaspoon ground cinnamon
¼ teaspoon ground nutmeg
¼ teaspoon ground cloves
2 packets of Stevia Powder
6 tablespoons salted butter
¾ cup water

Preheat oven to 350 degrees. Wash and core apples. Peel the skin down from the top about one inch. Level the bottoms and arrange in a baking dish. Combine spices, stevia and butter. Fill each apple with a tablespoon of mixture. In a baking dish filled with water, bake for 40-50 minutes, basting often until tender.

Makes 6 servings.

Green Apples in Nut Butter

1/3 cup almond or cashew butter
5 to 6 drops of Stevia
8 oz. cream cheese, softened at room temperature
2 tablespoons goat's milk

In a medium-sized bowl, combine almond or cashew butter with Stevia and mix well with an electric mixer. Beat in the cream cheese and then the milk. Add a little more milk if the mixture seems too thick. Serve immediately, or cover and refrigerate until ready to serve. Serve with sliced apples, whole fresh strawberries or both.

Makes 1¾ cup.

Debbie's Fruit Bowl

Thanks go to Debbie Percle for this recipe. Serve it as a snack, or for breakfast.

2 Granny Smith apples, cored and cut into large chunks
1 cup (10) strawberries, halved and sliced
1¾ cup blueberries
½ teaspoon cinnamon
½ cup pecan pieces (chopped)
½ cup plain yogurt
1 tablespoon melted butter
¾ teaspoon lemon peel
1 tablespoon lemon juice
½ cup fresh-grated coconut
Stevia to taste

Wash, core and dice apples. Sprinkle well with lemon juice to prevent them from browning. Combine apple pieces with strawberries and blue berries.

In a separate bowl, combine yogurt, cinnamon, butter, lemon peel, coconut and Stevia. Fold this mixture in with the fruits and chill for 20 minutes. Serve topped with pecans and cinnamon.

Makes 4-6 servings.

Roasted Pecans

You can roast all types of nuts using this recipe.

2 tablespoons melted butter
2 cups pecan halves (or other nuts)
Seasoning salt, if desired

Preheat oven to 250 degrees. In a small bowl, toss the pecans lightly in melted butter and spread them out evenly on a baking sheet. Roast for 30 to 45 minutes, or until you begin to smell the pecans. Watch carefully — nuts burn easily.
Makes 8 servings.

Roasted Chestnuts

This is a great snack for when you're craving something salty.

1 pound chestnuts
¼ cup butter
salt to taste
1 pinch ground cinnamon

Preheat oven to 375 degrees. Cut a ½ inch crisscross incision on the flat side of each nut. Take care to cut through the shells to prevent the nuts from exploding. Place in a shallow baking pan and bake for 25-30 minutes. Peel off the shell.

Place nuts in a skillet with butter and sauté over high heat until the butter is melted and the chestnuts are well coated. Place skillet in oven and roast nuts until they are golden on top. Sprinkle with cinnamon, salt and serve.
Makes 16 servings (1 pound).

Cinnamon Roasted Almonds

This easy snack is great for serving any time, or at holiday parties.

1 egg white
1 teaspoon cold water
4 cups whole almonds
¼ cup Stevia powder
¼ teaspoon salt
½ teaspoon ground cinnamon

Preheat oven to 250 degrees. Lightly beat the egg white. Add water and beat again until frothy, but not stiff. Add nuts and stir until well coated. Separately, combine Stevia, salt, and cinnamon and sprinkle over nuts. Toss to coat and spread evenly on a lightly greased, 10x15 inch jelly roll pan. Bake for 1 hour until golden, turning occasionally. Cool and store in an airtight container.

Makes 16 servings (4 cups)

Frosted Pecan Bites

This dish is great for snacking, or for a festive, holiday occasion.

1 pound pecan halves
½ cup butter
¼ cup powdered Stevia
2 egg whites, stiffly beaten
1 pinch salt

Preheat oven to 275 degrees. Bake pecans for 10-15 minutes or until lightly toasted. Set aside to cool. Fold stevia, salt and pecans into egg whites. Increase oven temperature to 325 degrees. Melt butter or margarine on a baking sheet. Spread the nut mixture even over the pan and bake for 30 minutes, stirring every 10 minutes. Remove from oven and cool.

Makes 6 servings (6 cups).

Caramel Apple Substitute

Green apples, sliced
Honey
Chopped almonds

Roll green apple slices in honey, and then in chopped almonds. Lay out on wax paper to harden.

Doug Kaufmann's Antifungal Eating Plan

I. The Initial Phase Diet

(formerly the *Phase One Diet*)

Food Groups	Foods ALLOWED on the diet	Foods EXCLUDED from the diet
1. Sugar	None[a]	All sugars excluded
2. Artificial and herbal sweeteners	Stevia, Stevia Plus	Aspartame, saccharin
3. Fruit	Green apples, berries, avocados, grapefruit, lemons, limes and fresh coconut	All others, including fruit juices
4. Meat	Virtually all meats, including fish, poultry and beef[b]	Breaded meats
5. Eggs	Yes, all types allowed	Avoid egg substitutes
6. Dairy[c]	Butter and yogurt (organic is best); sparingly: cream cheese, organic, unsweetened whipping cream, and real, sour cream	All others, including margarine and any of the butter substitutes
7. Vegetables	Most fresh, unblemished vegetables and freshly made vegetable juice[d]	Potatoes and legumes (beans and peas)
8. Beverages	Bottled or filtered water; non-fruity, herb teas; Stevia-sweetened, fresh lemonade or lime-ade	Coffee and tea (including decaf) and regular/diet sodas
9. Grains	Zero grains allowed	Pasta, rice, corn, wheat, quinoa, amaranth, millet, buckwheat, oats and barley
10. Yeast products	No yeast allowed	All are all *excluded*, as are bread, mushrooms, pastries and alcohol
11. Vinegars	Unpasteurized, apple cider vinegar and black olives not aged in vinegar	Pickles, salad dressings[e] green olives, soy sauce
12. Oils	Olive, grape or flax seed, and virgin coconut (cold-pressed is best)	Partially-hydrogenated ("trans") oils, corn and peanut oil
13. Nuts	Raw nuts, including pecans, almonds, walnuts, cashews, pumpkin seeds	Peanuts (and all peanut products) and pistachios are excluded.

II. InterPhase

(formerly the *Phase Two Diet*)

Food Groups	Foods ALLOWED in the diet	Foods EXCLUDED from the diet
1. Sugar	Same as *Initial Phase Diet* for food groups number one through six.	
2. Artificial and herbal sweeteners		
3. Fruit		
4. Meat		
5. Eggs		
6. Dairy[c]		
7. Vegetables	Fresh, unblemished vegetables and freshly made vegetable juice,[d] *yams, legumes (beans and peas)*	Potatoes
8. Beverages	Bottled/filtered water; non-fruity, herb teas; Stevia-sweetened, fresh lemonade or lime-ade	Coffee and tea (including decaf) and sodas (diet sodas also excluded)
9. Grains	*Oats (oatmeal), brown rice, quinoa, amaranth, millet, buckwheat, barley, flour tortillas, sourdough bread* (in moderation)	Corn and yeast breads
10. Yeast Products	Same as *Initial Phase Diet* for food groups number ten through thirteen.	
11. Vinegars		
12. Oils		
13. Nuts		

Notes for Initial Phase and InterPhase

a. Honey may be used sparingly as a sweetener if needed.

b. Farm-raised meat and fish are corn-fed, so they should be kept to a minimum. Grass-fed beef is ideal, followed by organic meats for which antibiotic exposure has been minimized.

c. Dairy products are better if from range-fed cattle and animals not injected with antibiotics, hormones or steroids, nor fed with silo-stored grains. Good products include Brown Cow, Monarch Hills and Redwood Hills. Whipping cream is liquid, unsweetened, heavy cream.

d. Organically grown vegetables are preferred.

e. Excluded because many of them are fermented products.

III. LifePhase for Health Maintenance

Food Groups	Foods that are ENCOURAGED	Foods that are DISCOURAGED
1. Sugars	Honey (as necessary)	Caution with all sugars, especially corn and fructose sweeteners
2. Artificial and herbal sweeteners	Stevia, Stevia Plus	Aspartame, saccharin
3. Fruit	Green apples, berries, avocados, fresh coconut, grapefruit, lemons, limes and other citris fruits, and their juices.	Minimize bananas and melons. Avoid processed juices. Babies do not need to drink juice. Dried fruits in bulk storage bins run a high risk for fungal contamination.
4. Meat	Virtually all meats, including fish, poultry and beef and even breaded cuts. Grass fed beef is best.	Farm raised and grain-fed mean corn-fed, so watch for this on the label, and be cautious.
5. Eggs	Yes, all eggs are allowed	Avoid egg substitutes.
6. Dairy	Yogurt (especially goat yogurt) Gouda cheese, cream cheese, unsweetened whipping cream, sour cream made from real cream, butter, goat's milk, organic, hormone free cow's milk.	Avoid margarine, which is not a dairy product, and *trans* fatty acids.
7. Vegetables	Eat lots of fresh, unblemished vegetables and freshly made vegetable juice. Yams and legumes (beans and peas) are fine, as are potatoes when eaten in moderation.	Corn and corn products should be minimized for life. Mushrooms are fungi, NOT vegetables.
8. Beverages	Bottled/filtered water; non-fruity, herb teas; Stevia-sweetened, fresh lemonade or lime-ade. Sparkling mineral waters are excellent. Green tea is good for you.	Coffee and tea should be drunk sparingly. Sodas remain excluded, as do most sports drinks, which are high in sugar.

LifePhase (continued)

Food Groups	Foods that are ENCOURAGED	Foods that are DISCOURAGED
9. Grains	Oats (oatmeal), rice of any kind, quinoa, amaranth, millet, buckwheat, barley, flour tortillas, sourdough bread. Aside from oats and rice, pasta likely remains the best source of grains, because scientists maintain you filter out mycotoxins when you drain the boiled water.	Grains, organic or otherwise, should be eaten in moderation, especially when they come in the form of yeast-raised breads. This is true regardless of whether the grain is "whole" or not.
10. Yeast Products	None.	Try to avoid mushrooms, alcohol, fermented soy products and yeast breads. Also, try to avoid foods that list yeast as an ingredient.
11. Vinegars	Unpasteurized, apple cider vinegar is best to use in dressings etc.	Caution with fermented foods such as pickles.
12. Oils	Olive, grape seed, flax seed etc. Use cold pressed oils when available. Omega 3 fatty acids are excellent when taken as supplements (flax seed, fish oils, evening primrose oil, shark liver oil etc.)	Partially-hydrogenated ("trans") oils, corn and peanut oil
13. Nuts	Raw nuts, including pecans, almonds, walnuts, cashews, pumpkin seeds and sunflower seeds. These are great snacks. Almond and cashew butters are excellent replacements for peanut butter.	Peanuts (and all peanut products) and pistacios are excluded, along with any obviously damaged or moldy nuts of the recommended sorts.

Doug Kaufmann

Foods to Avoid

Ten foods commonly contaminated with mycotoxins

Alcoholic beverages

Alcohol is the mycotoxin of the Saccharomyces yeast- brewer's yeast. Other mycotoxins can also be introduced, through the use of mold-contaminated grains and fruits. That's because producers of alcoholic beverages often use grains too contaminated with fungi and mycotoxins for use as table foods. So, chances are that your beer or wine contains more than just alcohol.[1] Before you drink for the health of your heart, consider the other, possible risks of drinking — there are safer ways of consuming antioxidants.

Corn

Corn is "universally contaminated" with fumonisin and other fungal toxins such as aflatoxin, zearalenone and ochratoxin.[2] Fumonisin and aflatoxin are known for their cancer-causing effects, while zearalenone and ochratoxin can cause estrogenic and kidney-related problems, respectively. Unfortunately, corn is even more of a staple in our diets than you might think. For example, chicken nuggets consist of corn-fed chicken covered by a corn-based batter that has been sweetened with corn syrup.

Wheat

Wheat and the products made from wheat — breads, cereals and pasta — is another often contaminated staple. Pasta may be the least "offensive" form of the grain, since certain water-soluble mycotoxins such as deoxynivalenol are partially removed and discarded when the water in which the pasta was cooked is tossed out. On the other hand, traces of more harmful, heat stable and fat soluble mycotoxins, such as aflatoxin, remain in the grain. Regarding breads — it probably doesn't matter if it's organic, inorganic, sprouted, blessed or not — if it came from a grain that has been stored for months in a silo, chances are it's been contaminated with fungi and mycotoxins.

Barley

Similar to other grains that can be damaged by drought, floods and harvesting and storage processes, barley is equally susceptible to contamination by mycotoxin-producing fungi. Barley is used in the production of various cereals and alcoholic beverages.

Sugar (sugar cane and sugar beets)

Not only are sugar cane and sugar beets often contaminated with fungi and their associated fungi, but they, like the other grains, fuel the growth of fungi. Fungi need carbohydrates — sugars — to thrive.

Sorghum

Sorghum is used in a variety of grain-based products intended for both humans and animals. It is also used in the production of alcoholic beverages.

Peanuts

A 1993 study demonstrated that 24 different types of fungi had colonized the insides of the peanuts tested.[3] And that was after the exterior of the peanut was sterilized! So, when you choose to eat peanuts, not only are you potentially eating these molds, but also their mycotoxins. Incidentally, in the same study, the examiners found 23 different fungi on the insides of corn kernels tested. In case you're thinking to plant your own garden in order to obtain non-contaminated corn or peanuts, it does no good if the seed (kernel) used for planting is already riddled with mold.

Rye

The same goes for rye as for wheat and other grains. In addition, when we use wheat and rye to make bread, we add two other products that compound our fungal concerns: sugar and yeast!

Cottonseed

Cottonseed is found typically in the oil form — cottonseed oil — but it is also used in its grain form for many animal foods. Several studies have shown that cottonseed is highly and often-contaminated with mycotoxins.

Hard cheeses

Here's a hint: if you see mold growing throughout your cheese, no matter what you paid for it, there's a pretty good chance that there's a mycotoxin not far from the mold. It is estimated that each fungus on Earth produces up to 3 different mycotoxins. The total number of mycotoxins known to date numbers in the thousands.

On the other hand, some cheeses, such as Gouda cheese, are made with yogurt-type of cultures — Lactobacillus, etc. — and not fungi.[3] These cheeses are a much healthier alternative, fungally-speaking.

1. Council for Agricultural Science and technology. Mycotoxins: Economic and Health Risks. Task Force Report Number 116. CAST. Ames, IA. Nov 1989).

2. Council for Agricultural Science and Technology. Mycotoxins: Risks in Plant, Animal and Human Systems. Task Force Report No. 139. Ames, IA. Jan 2003.

3. Costantini, A. Etiology and Prevention of Atherosclerosis. Fungalbionics Series. 1998/99).

Assessing Fungi's Impact on Your Health

The following is the latest in a series of questionnaires Doug and Dr. Dave have used for the past 30 years. Based upon research concerning known, fungal risk factors, the questionnaire is used to assess the degree to which patients may have been exposed to fungi, and the odds that the microbes (or their mycotoxins) lie behind a given problem.

Medical History

yes no

❐ ❐ 1. At any time in your life, have you taken repeated or prolonged rounds of antibiotics?

If so, how long were you on the antibiotics, and for what conditions?

❐ ❐ 2. Are you allergic to any medications? Please specify.

❐ ❐ 3. At any time in your life, have you taken repeated or prolonged courses of steroids or cortisone-based pills? If so, for what?

❐ ❐ 4. Have you been diagnosed with fibromyalgia?

❐ ❐ 5. Do you have, or have you ever had asthma?

❐ ❐ 6. Have you been diagnosed with arthritis?

❐ ❐ 7. Do you have diabetes? Type I or Type II (circle please)?

❐ ❐ 8. At any time in your life, have you been treated for worms or parasites?

❐ ❐ 9. Have you traveled outside of the U.S.? When and where?

❐ ❐ 10. Have you ever had cancer?

If so, did you undergo chemotherapy or radiation treatment?

❐ ❐ 11. Have you had ringworm, jock itch, fingernail or toenail fungus? (circle please)

❐ ❐ Do you suffer from any of these problems at present?

yes no

❒ ❒ 12. Have you ever been diagnosed with attention-deficit disorder (ADD or ADHD)? List any medications you are currently taking for this.

❒ ❒ 13. Had you spent time in or near construction sites when you became ill?

General health evaluation

❒ ❒ 14. Do you suffer from fatigue? Circle your energy level (10 is lowest).
10 9 8 7 6 5 4 3 2 1

❒ ❒ 15. Do you often feel irritable?

❒ ❒ 16. Do you often feel dazed or "spaced out?"

❒ ❒ 17. Do you suffer from memory loss?

❒ ❒ 18. Do your muscles, bones, or joints bother you? (circle all that apply)
Would you describe them as aching, weak, stiff, or swollen? (circle please)

❒ ❒ 19. Do you get more than the occasional headache? How long has this been so?

a. What type have you been diagnosed with (migraine, tension etc.)?

b. How many days a week do you get headaches?

❒ ❒ c. Do they feel as though they might be caused by a hormone imbalance?

d. What medications do you take for your headaches?

❒ ❒ 20. Do you have itching, tingling, or burning skin? (circle please)

❒ ❒ 21. Do you have hives, psoriasis, dandruff, or chronic skin rashes? (circle please)

❒ ❒ 22. Do you have acne?

❒ ❒ 23. Are you on medications for the above skin problems? Name them, and how long you have taken them.

❒ ❒ 24. Do you suffer from hair loss?

❒ ❒ 25. Do your inner ears itch?

❒ ❒ 26. Does your vision blur for no apparent reason?

yes no

❐ ❐ 27. Have you been diagnosed with high or low blood pressure? (circle please)

❐ ❐ 28. Have you been diagnosed with high cholesterol or triglycerides? (circle please)

❐ ❐ 29. List medications you take for blood pressure, cholesterol or triglycerides. Include how long you have taken them.

❐ ❐ 30. Do you have mitral valve prolapse, a racing pulse or an uncontrolled heart beat? List medications you take for this condition, including how long you have taken them.

❐ ❐ 32. Have you ever been diagnosed with an autoimmune disease? Specify the disease, including when you were diagnosed.

❐ ❐ 33. Are you bothered by recurring problems with your digestive tract such as bloating, belching, gas, constipation, diarrhea, abdominal pain, indigestion, or reflux? (circle please)

List any medications you take for your condition, including length of dosage.

❐ ❐ 34. Have you taken multiple prescriptions of antibiotics for a chronic infection?

Describe the infections, including their duration and frequency.

❐ ❐ 35. Does your health problem get worse in response to heat? For example, does a shower, bath, or very hot weather make it worse? (circle please)

❐ ❐ 36. Do your symptoms worsen on damp days, or when you spend time in musty/moldy environments?

❐ ❐ 37. On days when the mold/pollen count is elevated, do you feel worse?

❐ ❐ 38. Do you often feel more unhappy than "normal" for a given situation?

❐ ❐ 39. Have you been diagnosed with depression?

❐ ❐ a.Are you presently seeing a therapist for depression?

b. List any medications you take for depression, including how long you have taken them.

yes no

❐ ❐ 40. Do you drink alcohol?

a. How many times a week do you usually drink?

b. How much do you drink on these occasions?

c. For how long have you drunk alcohol?

❐ ❐ d. Have you ever gotten drunk on a regular basis?

❐ ❐ 41. Do you smoke cigarettes?

a. How many cigarettes a day do you usually smoke?

b. How many years have you smoked?

❐ ❐ c. Do (or did) your parents or spouse often smoke around you?

❐ ❐ 42. Have you had sharp cravings for corn, peanuts, or sugar? (circle please)

❐ ❐ 43. Have you spent time on a farm? How long ago, and for how long?

❐ ❐ 44. Has your home or office ever had a mold problem?

❐ ❐ Has either ever been flooded to any degree?

Allergies

❐ ❐ 45. Do you suffer allergic reactions to pollens, molds, animal dander, dust, mites, perfumes, chemical, smoke, or fabric store odors? (circle please)

46. List any allergy injections, and the length of time on them.

❐ ❐ 47. Are you allergic to any foods?

a. Have you had food allergy tests run?

b. Were these skin tests or blood tests? (circle please)

For women only

❐ ❐ 48. Are you 1)currently taking or 2)have you ever taken birth control pills? (circle please)

❐ ❐ Have you suffered complications as a result? Describe them.

❐ ❐ 49. Have you experienced uterine, vaginal or urinary tract problems such as endometriosis, polycystic ovarian syndrome or fibroids (circle, specifying if not listed)?

yes no

❐ ❐ 50. Are your ovaries, thyroid gland, adrenals or pancreas malfunctioning? (circle please)

51. Among the following symptoms of possible hormone disturbances, circle all you have experienced: PMS, menstrual irregularities, loss of libido, infertility, sugar cravings, weight problems, and often feeling hotter or colder than is normal for a given situation.

❐ ❐ Are you on medications for any these problems? List them, and the length of time for which you have been taking them.

For men only

❐ ❐ 48. Do you now—or have you ever—suffered pain in the testicles unrelated to trauma?

❐ ❐ 49. Have you ever been bothered by prostate problems?

❐ ❐ 50. Are your testicles, thryoid gland, adrenals or pancreas malfunctioning? (circle please)

❐ ❐ 51. Among the following symptoms of possible, hormone disturbances, circle all you have experienced: loss of libido, infertility, impotence, sugar cravings, weight problems, and often feeling hotter or colder than is normal for a given situation.

❐ ❐ Are you on medications for any of these conditions? List them, and the length of time for which you have been taking them.

We'd like to give you an exact risk assessment for X number of "yes" answers. The problem is, things aren't quite that simple. For example, say you answer "no" to every question above, with the exception of a "yes" for being on antibiotics for six months at one stage of your life. That one "yes" — combined with a weight problem — would suggest to us that you should get on the Initial Phase diet for at least a couple of weeks, in addition to following our Antifungal Program.

Having said the above, in our experience, more "yes" answers do tend to indicate a more serious degree of fungal infection and/or exposure to mycotoxins.

A Week of the Initial Phase Diet

Example menus

Initial Phase differs so much from what the average American eats that we've gotten a lot of questions as to what a menu based on the diet would look like. The layout below is not meant to be followed verbatim. And, remember, *Initial Phase* almost always requires more than a week to achieve results. Please note the emphasis on water, and refer to our recipe section/website for details on certain dishes.

Monday

Breakfast:	Fried eggs, uncured bacon, grapefruit
Snack:	Almonds, water (always bottled or filtered)
Lunch:	Tuna with celery. Herbal tea
Snack:	Carrot sticks, water
Dinner:	Steak, steamed veggies, sparkling lime water
Dessert: (optional)	Plain yogurt with raspberries

Tuesday

Breakfast:	Omelet with onions, leeks, parsley, and chopped bacon
Snack:	Celery sticks, water
Lunch:	Chicken salad with Phase I dressing
Snack:	Cashews, water
Dinner:	Salmon fillets with lemon and butter, avocado salad
Dessert: (optional)	Green apple

Wednesday

Breakfast:	Poached eggs, freshly squeezed carrot juice
Snack:	Walnuts, water
Lunch:	Broccoli chicken without rice, herbal tea
Snack:	Grapefruit, water
Dinner:	Steak, spinach salad with lemon juice and olive oil dressing
Dessert: (optional)	Plain yogurt with chopped pecans and fresh cranberries

Thursday

Breakfast:	Scrambled eggs with breakfast steak
Snack:	Green apple wedges, almonds, herbal tea
Lunch:	Tuna salad with lettuce
Snack:	Broccoli, cauliflower, water
Dinner:	Halibut with sautéed vegetables
Dessert: (optional)	Yogurt with fresh blueberries

Friday

Breakfast:	Freshly squeezed carrot juice, hard boiled eggs
Snack:	Celery sticks or green apple wedges with almond butter
Lunch:	Beef patties, steamed and buttered asparagus
Snack:	Sunflower seeds, water
Dinner:	Kaufmann's favorite meal (see recipes)
Dessert: (optional)	grapefruit

Saturday

Breakfast:	Omelet with green onions, bacon, spinach leaves
Snack:	Carrot sticks
Lunch:	Cucumber salad w/ onions, tomatoes, black olives, olive oil
Snack:	Pecans, yogurt with blackberries, water
Dinner:	Steak with steamed broccoli
Dessert: (optional)	Sautéed green apples and cranberries with roasted pecans and whipping cream

Sunday

Breakfast:	Freshly squeezed carrot juice, grapefruit, poached eggs
Snack:	Pumpkin seeds, water
Lunch:	Salad with grilled tuna, herbal tea
Snack:	Celery sticks, water
Dinner:	Stir-fried chicken, broccoli, snow peas, squash with butter
Dessert: (optional)	Almonds, chamomile tea

Shopping List

Make copies of this list for ease in making notes
as you plan meals, prior to shopping.

Stevia

Honey

Green apples

Berries

Avocados

Grapefruit

Lemons

Limes

Chicken

Beef

Turkey

Pork

Seafood

Sausage and/or Bacon

Cold cuts

Eggs

Shopping List

Yogurt

Cream Cheese

Whipping Cream

Sour Cream

Butter

Vegetables

Spices

Bottled water

Herbal Tea

Vegetable juice

Apple Cider Vinegar (unpasteurized)

Olive oil

Grapefruit Seed Oil

Flax Seeds

Macadamia Nut Oil

Coconut Oil

Raw nuts (no peanuts or pistachios)

Testimonies

Dear Doug,
I want to thank you for your courage and persistency in the face of the pharmaceutical giants and the medical community. I really enjoy your show and having Dave and Jami adds so much. I call you guys "The Fab 3!" You have created an excitement in me that has energized me to take charge of my health.

In early 2000, I went for a checkup with my doctor and my cholesterol as well as blood pressure had skyrocketed. The blood pressure medication drove me into severe depression. I had problems with the side effects of many of my medications.

Once I began watching your show, my health literacy truly increased. The result of the knowledge that you imparted to me led me to follow the phase one diet and take natural supplements. Since I have made the changes, I have an overall better feeling. My blood pressure has returned to normal and I no longer take the medication. My sense of smell has improved. My cholesterol decreased. My toenail fungus is gone. I now have confidence.

God Bless You 3!
-S

Dear Doug,
My wife and I went on the phase one diet last year. She has lost 45 pounds and has been able to stop taking two of four prescriptions that she was on, per her doctor's advice. I have lost 67 pounds and completely off of drugs for high blood pressure, acid reflux and pain. We have both given up our "fat clothes!" Thank you for your knowledge, and may God Bless You and Your Family.
-C

Dear Doug,
The last time we spoke was a year ago. I was close to death, no longer able to work, and in tears. Now, I'm on the Phase One Diet, I'm working again, I'm on the road to recovery, I've lost 35 pounds and feel better than I have in years. I thank you for letting God work through you.
-C

Dear Doug,
For most of my life, I was totally ignorant of how nutrition, or the lack of it, directly affected my heath. The birth of my first child set in motion a chain of events that impacted my life in a negative way. I had gained 130 pounds and I had no life. In February, I lost over 100 pounds and went from a size 26 to a size 6. I am maintaining my weight through proper diet and exercise. I share this testimony hoping that it will bring light to people who are living in darkness. My prayer is that others will have the faith and courage to take charge of their own lives. I want them to know that they CAN do it. Thank you, Doug, for being who you are and for swimming against the current.
-M

Dear Doug,
I have been on the phase 1 diet now for almost a month and I am feeling so much better. I have more energy than I have had in a long time. Wow! I know I am getting better! I am so grateful God lead me to your program.
Thank you so much.
-R

Dear Doug,
I have been watching and taping your show. The information that you have presented has been a lifesaver for me. Since last October, I have got off of all of my prescriptions for asthma, high blood pressure, high cholesterol, and G.E.R.D. (Gastro-Esophageal Reflux Disease) under my doctor's supervision. I have been on the Phase One and Two Diets and have lost 20 pounds. God Bless All of You, and Keep Up the Good Work,
-B

Dear Doug,
I have a friend who suffers from depression so much that they were speaking of giving her shock treatments. She has suffered from this for 15 years. To make a long story short, she is on your diet. After 3 weeks, she is a new person. From my point of view, I have never seen her look and act so good. She has a true smile on her face. God is good to have sent your knowledge.
Sincerely,
-B

Dear Doug,
I am a long time listener. You gave me advice on my mother who had cancer of the colon. The cancer had spread to her lymph nodes. She was 83 at the time. We followed your advice regarding diet and supplements to the letter. She has been cancer free for 3 years and feels better today than she did 20 years ago.
-B

Dear Reader,
My aunt had been suffering from serious digestive tract problems for months. She'd been to several local family practice physicians in her area, and she'd even seen one of the top gastroenterologists in the

country. None of them could discover what was causing either her pain or her constipation. Tests generated negative results for a number of possibilities, including irritable bowel disease, inflammatory bowel disease, ulcerative colitis, Crohn's disease, polyps, diverticulitis and bowel obstruction. Cancer was ruled out, as well.

Despite failure to determine the cause of my aunt's problems, she was prescribed more than 20 drugs before the decision was finally made to cut 12 inches from her colon. It was explained to her that the surgery would make her bowel contractions more effective. My aunt listened to her doctors' advice and went ahead with the surgery. Afterwards, she only got sicker.

My aunt noticed at one point that drinking milk tended to exacerbate her situation. So, she asked the specialists if that and other things she was eating might not have something to do with her problems. Perhaps if she made some changes...? The specialists came back with an emphatic "no." They did say, however, that an even more drastic surgical procedure called a colostomy might be worth a try. A colostomy involves creating an opening between the colon and the abdominal wall. Food on its way through the colon is diverted through a stoma and into an external colostomy bag. Voila — no constipation!

Enter Doug Kaufmann. Doug consulted with my aunt and advised her to get on his *Initial Phase* diet and to begin the *Kaufmann Antifungal Program*. My aunt followed his advice. Within a week, months of agony ended, and she began to heal.

I continue to be moved by Doug's passion and drive to equip as many people as he can with the tools and philosophy they need to get and stay healthy.
-JC

Index of Ingredients

In addition to basil, oregano, paprika, parsley and thyme (these both fresh and dried), butter, garlic cloves, lemons and lemon juice, olive oil and onions appear in a very large number of the recipes found in this book. Because of this, they are not indexed below.

C

R

S

About Doug Kaufmann

Doug Kaufmann is a nationally recognized author, lecturer and television show host, with more than 30 years of experience in diversified health care.

Kaufmann served as a Navy hospital corpsman in Vietnam, where he was honored with the Combat Action Ribbon, Vietnamese Cross of Gallantry and the Vietnam Service Medal with one bronze star.

A group of Texan physicians recruited Kaufmann in 1987, having become interested in the lab technology he'd developed in L.A. During subsequent studies, many patients with "incurable" diseases responded favorably to dietary changes and antifungal drugs.

Kaufmann first introduced the philosophy behind these results on radio in 1992. At one time, his vignettes were carried by more than 600 stations. Kaufmann transitioned to television in 1999, where he continues to host his own health show.

About Jami Clark, R.N.

Jami Clark is certified in both Advanced Cardiac Life Support and Chemotherapy/Biotherapy. She has spent much of her nursing career in oncology and hematology.

When not working, she spends her time volunteering at teen pregnancy centers, homeless shelters and battered-women shelters in the Dallas area. She has also received recognition for her volunteer work with AIDS services of North Texas.

Jami is married with two children. She attends Collin Creek Free Will Baptist Church in Plano, Texas, where she is actively involved in Cuba mission work.